TEACHER'S GUIDE

Connected Mathematics 2

The Shapes of Algebra

Linear Systems and Inequalities

Glenda Lappan
James T. Fey
William M. Fitzgerald
Susan N. Friel
Elizabeth Difanis Phillips

PEARSON

Boston, Massachusetts · Glenview, Illinois · Shoreview, Minnesota · Upper Saddle River, New Jersey

Connected Mathematics™ was developed at Michigan State University with financial support from the Michigan State University Office of the Provost, Computing and Technology, and the College of Natural Science.

 This material is based upon work supported by the National Science Foundation under Grant No. MDR 9150217 and Grant No. ESI 9986372. Opinions expressed are those of the authors and not necessarily those of the Foundation.

The Michigan State University authors and administration have agreed that all MSU royalties arising from this publication will be devoted to purposes supported by the Department of Mathematics and the MSU Mathematics Enrichment Fund.

13-digit ISBN 978-0-13-366208-5
10-digit ISBN 0-13-366208-X
3 4 5 6 7 8 9 10 V011 11 10

Authors of Connected Mathematics

(from left to right) Glenda Lappan, Betty Phillips, Susan Friel, Bill Fitzgerald, Jim Fey

Glenda Lappan is a University Distinguished Professor in the Department of Mathematics at Michigan State University. Her research and development interests are in the connected areas of students' learning of mathematics and mathematics teachers' professional growth and change related to the development and enactment of K–12 curriculum materials.

James T. Fey is a Professor of Curriculum and Instruction and Mathematics at the University of Maryland. His consistent professional interest has been development and research focused on curriculum materials that engage middle and high school students in problem-based collaborative investigations of mathematical ideas and their applications.

William M. Fitzgerald (*Deceased*) was a Professor in the Department of Mathematics at Michigan State University. His early research was on the use of concrete materials in supporting student learning and led to the development of teaching materials for laboratory environments. Later he helped develop a teaching model to support student experimentation with mathematics.

Susan N. Friel is a Professor of Mathematics Education in the School of Education at the University of North Carolina at Chapel Hill. Her research interests focus on statistics education for middle-grade students and, more broadly, on teachers' professional development and growth in teaching mathematics K–8.

Elizabeth Difanis Phillips is a Senior Academic Specialist in the Mathematics Department of Michigan State University. She is interested in teaching and learning mathematics for both teachers and students. These interests have led to curriculum and professional development projects at the middle school and high school levels, as well as projects related to the teaching and learning of algebra across the grades.

CMP2 Development Staff

Teacher Collaborator in Residence
Yvonne Grant
Michigan State University

Production and Field Site Manager
Lisa Keller
Michigan State University

Administrative Assistant
Judith Martus Miller
Michigan State University

Technical and Editorial Support
Brin Keller, Peter Lappan, Jim Laser,
Michael Masterson, Stacey Miceli

Assessment Team
June Bailey and **Debra Sobko** (Apollo Middle School, Rochester, New York), **George Bright** (University of North Carolina, Greensboro), **Gwen Ranzau Campbell** (Sunrise Park Middle School, White Bear Lake, Minnesota), **Holly DeRosia, Kathy Dole,** and **Teri Keusch** (Portland Middle School, Portland, Michigan), **Mary Beth Schmitt** (Traverse City East Junior High School, Traverse City, Michigan), **Genni Steele** (Central Middle School, White Bear Lake, Minnesota), **Jacqueline Stewart** (Okemos, Michigan), **Elizabeth Tye** (Magnolia Junior High School, Magnolia, Arkansas)

Development Assistants
At Lansing Community College *Undergraduate Assistant:* **James Brinegar**

At Michigan State University *Graduate Assistants:* **Dawn Berk, Emily Bouck, Bulent Buyukbozkirli, Kuo-Liang Chang, Christopher Danielson, Srinivasa Dharmavaram, Deb Johanning, Wesley Kretzschmar, Kelly Rivette, Sarah Sword, Tat Ming Sze, Marie Turini, Jeffrey Wanko;** *Undergraduate Assistants:* **Daniel Briggs, Jeffrey Chapin, Jade Corsé, Elisha Hardy, Alisha Harold, Elizabeth Keusch, Julia Letoutchaia, Karen Loeffler, Brian Oliver, Carl Oliver, Evonne Pedawi, Lauren Rebrovich**

At the University of Maryland *Graduate Assistants:* **Kim Harris Bethea, Kara Karch**

At the University of North Carolina (Chapel Hill) *Graduate Assistants:* **Mark Ellis, Trista Stearns;** *Undergraduate Assistant:* **Daniel Smith**

Advisory Board for CMP2

Thomas Banchoff
Professor of Mathematics
Brown University
Providence, Rhode Island

Anne Bartel
Mathematics Coordinator
Minneapolis Public Schools
Minneapolis, Minnesota

Hyman Bass
Professor of Mathematics
University of Michigan
Ann Arbor, Michigan

Joan Ferrini-Mundy
Associate Dean of the College of
Natural Science; Professor
Michigan State University
East Lansing, Michigan

James Hiebert
Professor
University of Delaware
Newark, Delaware

Susan Hudson Hull
Charles A. Dana Center
University of Texas
Austin, Texas

Michele Luke
Mathematics Curriculum
Coordinator
West Junior High
Minnetonka, Minnesota

Kay McClain
Assistant Professor of
Mathematics Education
Vanderbilt University
Nashville, Tennessee

Edward Silver
Professor; Chair of Educational
Studies
University of Michigan
Ann Arbor, Michigan

Judith Sowder
Professor Emerita
San Diego State University
San Diego, California

Lisa Usher
Mathematics Resource Teacher
California Academy of
Mathematics and Science
San Pedro, California

Field Test Sites for CMP2

During the development of the revised edition of *Connected Mathematics* (CMP2), more than 100 classroom teachers have field-tested materials at 49 school sites in 12 states and the District of Columbia. This classroom testing occurred over three academic years (2001 through 2004), allowing careful study of the effectiveness of each of the 24 units that comprise the program. A special thanks to the students and teachers at these pilot schools.

Arkansas
Magnolia Public Schools
Kittena Bell*, Judith Trowell*; *Central Elementary School:* Maxine Broom, Betty Eddy, Tiffany Fallin, Bonnie Flurry, Carolyn Monk, Elizabeth Tye; *Magnolia Junior High School:* Monique Bryan, Ginger Cook, David Graham, Shelby Lamkin

Colorado
Boulder Public Schools
Nevin Platt Middle School: Judith Koenig
St. Vrain Valley School District, Longmont
Westview Middle School: Colleen Beyer, Kitty Canupp, Ellie Decker*, Peggy McCarthy, Tanya deNobrega, Cindy Payne, Ericka Pilon, Andrew Roberts

District of Columbia
Capitol Hill Day School: Ann Lawrence

Georgia
University of Georgia, Athens
Brad Findell
Madison Public Schools
Morgan County Middle School: Renee Burgdorf, Lynn Harris, Nancy Kurtz, Carolyn Stewart

Maine
Falmouth Public Schools
Falmouth Middle School: Donna Erikson, Joyce Hebert, Paula Hodgkins, Rick Hogan, David Legere, Cynthia Martin, Barbara Stiles, Shawn Towle*

Michigan
Portland Public Schools
Portland Middle School: Mark Braun, Holly DeRosia, Kathy Dole*, Angie Foote, Teri Keusch, Tammi Wardwell
Traverse City Area Public Schools
Bertha Vos Elementary: Kristin Sak; *Central Grade School:* Michelle Clark; Jody Meyers; *Eastern Elementary:* Karrie Tufts; *Interlochen Elementary:* Mary McGee-Cullen; *Long Lake Elementary:* Julie Faulkner*, Charlie Maxbauer, Katherine Sleder; *Norris Elementary:* Hope Slanaker; *Oak Park Elementary:* Jessica Steed; *Traverse Heights Elementary:* Jennifer Wolfert; *Westwoods Elementary:* Nancy Conn; *Old Mission Peninsula School:* Deb Larimer; *Traverse City East Junior High:* Ivanka Berkshire, Ruthanne Kladder, Jan Palkowski, Jane Peterson, Mary Beth Schmitt; *Traverse City West Junior High:* Dan Fouch*, Ray Fouch
Sturgis Public Schools
Sturgis Middle School: Ellen Eisele

Minnesota
Burnsville School District 191
Hidden Valley Elementary: Stephanie Cin, Jane McDevitt
Hopkins School District 270
Alice Smith Elementary: Sandra Cowing, Kathleen Gustafson, Martha Mason, Scott Stillman; *Eisenhower Elementary:* Chad Bellig, Patrick Berger, Nancy Glades, Kye Johnson, Shane Wasserman, Victoria Wilson; *Gatewood Elementary:* Sarah Ham, Julie Kloos, Janine Pung, Larry Wade; *Glen Lake Elementary:* Jacqueline Cramer, Kathy Hering, Cecelia Morris, Robb Trenda; *Katherine Curren Elementary:* Diane Bancroft, Sue DeWit, John Wilson; *L. H. Tanglen Elementary:* Kevin Athmann, Lisa Becker, Mary LaBelle, Kathy Rezac, Roberta Severson; *Meadowbrook Elementary:* Jan Gauger, Hildy Shank, Jessica Zimmerman; *North Junior High:* Laurel Hahn, Kristin Lee, Jodi Markuson, Bruce Mestemacher, Laurel Miller, Bonnie Rinker, Jeannine Salzer, Sarah Shafer, Cam Stottler; *West Junior High:* Alicia Beebe, Kristie Earl, Nobu Fujii, Pam Georgetti, Susan Gilbert, Regina Nelson Johnson, Debra Lindstrom, Michele Luke*, Jon Sorensen
Minneapolis School District 1
Ann Sullivan K–8 School: Bronwyn Collins; Anne Bartel* (Curriculum and Instruction Office)
Wayzata School District 284
Central Middle School: Sarajane Myers, Dan Nielsen, Tanya Ravnholdt
White Bear Lake School District 624
Central Middle School: Amy Jorgenson, Michelle Reich, Brenda Sammon

New York
New York City Public Schools
IS 89: Yelena Aynbinder, Chi-Man Ng, Nina Rapaport, Joel Spengler, Phyllis Tam*, Brent Wyso; *Wagner Middle School:* Jason Appel, Intissar Fernandez, Yee Gee Get, Richard Goldstein, Irving Marcus, Sue Norton, Bernadita Owens, Jennifer Rehn*, Kevin Yuhas

---

* indicates a Field Test Site Coordinator

Ohio

Talawanda School District, Oxford
Talawanda Middle School: Teresa Abrams, Larry Brock, Heather Brosey, Julie Churchman, Monna Even, Karen Fitch, Bob George, Amanda Klee, Pat Meade, Sandy Montgomery, Barbara Sherman, Lauren Steidl
Miami University
Jeffrey Wanko*
Springfield Public Schools
Rockway School: Jim Mamer

Pennsylvania

Pittsburgh Public Schools
Kenneth Labuskes, Marianne O'Connor, Mary Lynn Raith*; *Arthur J. Rooney Middle School:* David Hairston, Stamatina Mousetis, Alfredo Zangaro; *Frick International Studies Academy:* Suzanne Berry, Janet Falkowski, Constance Finseth, Romika Hodge, Frank Machi; *Reizenstein Middle School:* Jeff Baldwin, James Brautigam, Lorena Burnett, Glen Cobbett, Michael Jordan, Margaret Lazur, Tamar McPherson, Melissa Munnell, Holly Neely, Ingrid Reed, Dennis Reft

Texas

Austin Independent School District
Bedichek Middle School: Lisa Brown, Jennifer Glasscock, Vicki Massey
El Paso Independent School District
Cordova Middle School: Armando Aguirre, Anneliesa Durkes, Sylvia Guzman, Pat Holguin*, William Holguin, Nancy Nava, Laura Orozco, Michelle Peña, Roberta Rosen, Patsy Smith, Jeremy Wolf
Plano Independent School District
Patt Henry, James Wohlgehagen*; *Frankford Middle School:* Mandy Baker, Cheryl Butsch, Amy Dudley, Betsy Eshelman, Janet Greene, Cort Haynes, Kathy Letchworth, Kay Marshall, Kelly McCants, Amy Reck, Judy Scott, Syndy Snyder, Lisa Wang; *Wilson Middle School:* Darcie Bane, Amanda Bedenko, Whitney Evans, Tonelli Hatley, Sarah (Becky) Higgs, Kelly Johnston, Rebecca McElligott, Kay Neuse, Cheri Slocum, Kelli Straight

Washington

Evergreen School District
Shahala Middle School: Nicole Abrahamsen, Terry Coon*, Carey Doyle, Sheryl Drechsler, George Gemma, Gina Helland, Amy Hilario, Darla Lidyard, Sean McCarthy, Tilly Meyer, Willow Nuewelt, Todd Parsons, Brian Pederson, Stan Posey, Shawn Scott, Craig Sjoberg, Lynette Sundstrom, Charles Switzer, Luke Youngblood

Wisconsin

Beaver Dam Unified School District
Beaver Dam Middle School: Jim Braemer, Jeanne Frick, Jessica Greatens, Barbara Link, Dennis McCormick, Karen Michels, Nancy Nichols*, Nancy Palm, Shelly Stelsel, Susan Wiggins

---

* indicates a Field Test Site Coordinator

Reviews of CMP to Guide Development of CMP2

Before writing for CMP2 began or field tests were conducted, the first edition of *Connected Mathematics* was submitted to the mathematics faculties of school districts from many parts of the country and to 80 individual reviewers for extensive comments.

School District Survey Reviews of CMP

Arizona
Madison School District #38 (Phoenix)

Arkansas
Cabot School District, Little Rock School District, Magnolia School District

California
Los Angeles Unified School District

Colorado
St. Vrain Valley School District (Longmont)

Florida
Leon County Schools (Tallahassee)

Illinois
School District #21 (Wheeling)

Indiana
Joseph L. Block Junior High (East Chicago)

Kentucky
Fayette County Public Schools (Lexington)

Maine
Selection of Schools

Massachusetts
Selection of Schools

Michigan
Sparta Area Schools

Minnesota
Hopkins School District

Texas
Austin Independent School District, The El Paso Collaborative for Academic Excellence, Plano Independent School District

Wisconsin
Platteville Middle School

Individual Reviewers of CMP

Arkansas
Deborah Cramer; Robby Frizzell (*Taylor*); Lowell Lynde (*University of Arkansas, Monticello*); Leigh Manzer (*Norfork*); Lynne Roberts (*Emerson High School, Emerson*); Tony Timms (*Cabot Public Schools*); Judith Trowell (*Arkansas Department of Higher Education*)

California
José Alcantar (*Gilroy*); Eugenie Belcher (*Gilroy*); Marian Pasternack (*Lowman M. S. T. Center, North Hollywood*); Susana Pezoa (*San Jose*); Todd Rabusin (*Hollister*); Margaret Siegfried (*Ocala Middle School, San Jose*); Polly Underwood (*Ocala Middle School, San Jose*)

Colorado
Janeane Golliher (*St. Vrain Valley School District, Longmont*); Judith Koenig (*Nevin Platt Middle School, Boulder*)

Florida
Paige Loggins (*Swift Creek Middle School, Tallahassee*)

Illinois
Jan Robinson (*School District #21, Wheeling*)

Indiana
Frances Jackson (*Joseph L. Block Junior High, East Chicago*)

Kentucky
Natalee Feese (*Fayette County Public Schools, Lexington*)

Maine
Betsy Berry (*Maine Math & Science Alliance, Augusta*)

Maryland
Joseph Gagnon (*University of Maryland, College Park*); Paula Maccini (*University of Maryland, College Park*)

Massachusetts
George Cobb (*Mt. Holyoke College, South Hadley*); Cliff Kanold (*University of Massachusetts, Amherst*)

Michigan
Mary Bouck (*Farwell Area Schools*); Carol Dorer (*Slauson Middle School, Ann Arbor*); Carrie Heaney (*Forsythe Middle School, Ann Arbor*); Ellen Hopkins (*Clague Middle School, Ann Arbor*); Teri Keusch (*Portland Middle School, Portland*); Valerie Mills (*Oakland Schools, Waterford*); Mary Beth Schmitt (*Traverse City East Junior High, Traverse City*); Jack Smith (*Michigan State University, East Lansing*); Rebecca Spencer (*Sparta Middle School, Sparta*); Ann Marie Nicoll Turner (*Tappan Middle School, Ann Arbor*); Scott Turner (*Scarlett Middle School, Ann Arbor*)

Minnesota
Margarita Alvarez (*Olson Middle School, Minneapolis*); Jane Amundson (*Nicollet Junior High, Burnsville*); Anne Bartel (*Minneapolis Public Schools*); Gwen Ranzau Campbell (*Sunrise Park Middle School, White Bear Lake*); Stephanie Cin (*Hidden Valley Elementary, Burnsville*); Joan Garfield (*University of Minnesota, Minneapolis*); Gretchen Hall (*Richfield Middle School, Richfield*); Jennifer Larson (*Olson Middle School, Minneapolis*); Michele Luke (*West Junior High, Minnetonka*); Jeni Meyer (*Richfield Junior High, Richfield*); Judy Pfingsten (*Inver Grove Heights Middle School, Inver Grove Heights*); Sarah Shafer (*North Junior High, Minnetonka*); Genni Steele (*Central Middle School, White Bear Lake*); Victoria Wilson (*Eisenhower Elementary, Hopkins*); Paul Zorn (*St. Olaf College, Northfield*)

New York
Debra Altenau-Bartolino (*Greenwich Village Middle School, New York*); Doug Clements (*University of Buffalo*); Francis Curcio (*New York University, New York*); Christine Dorosh (*Clinton School for Writers, Brooklyn*); Jennifer Rehn (*East Side Middle School, New York*); Phyllis Tam (*IS 89 Lab School, New York*); Marie Turini (*Louis Armstrong Middle School, New York*); Lucy West (*Community School District 2, New York*); Monica Witt (*Simon Baruch Intermediate School 104, New York*)

Pennsylvania
Robert Aglietti (*Pittsburgh*); Sharon Mihalich (*Freeport*); Jennifer Plumb (*South Hills Middle School, Pittsburgh*); Mary Lynn Raith (*Pittsburgh Public Schools*)

Texas
Michelle Bittick (*Austin Independent School District*); Margaret Cregg (*Plano Independent School District*); Sheila Cunningham (*Klein Independent School District*); Judy Hill (*Austin Independent School District*); Patricia Holguin (*El Paso Independent School District*); Bonnie McNemar (*Arlington*); Kay Neuse (*Plano Independent School District*); Joyce Polanco (*Austin Independent School District*); Marge Ramirez (*University of Texas at El Paso*); Pat Rossman (*Baker Campus, Austin*); Cindy Schimek (*Houston*); Cynthia Schneider (*Charles A. Dana Center, University of Texas at Austin*); Uri Treisman (*Charles A. Dana Center, University of Texas at Austin*); Jacqueline Weilmuenster (*Grapevine-Colleyville Independent School District*); LuAnn Weynand (*San Antonio*); Carmen Whitman (*Austin Independent School District*); James Wohlgehagen (*Plano Independent School District*)

Washington
Ramesh Gangolli (*University of Washington, Seattle*)

Wisconsin
Susan Lamon (*Marquette University, Hales Corner*); Steve Reinhart (*retired, Chippewa Falls Middle School, Eau Claire*)

Table of Contents

The Shapes of Algebra
Linear Systems and Inequalities

> The Student Edition pages for the Unit Opener follow page 16.

> The Student Edition pages for Investigation 1 follow page 30.

The Shapes of Algebra
Linear Systems and Inequalities

Goals of the Unit

- Write and use equations of circles

- Determine if lines are parallel or perpendicular by looking at patterns in their graphs, coordinates, and equations

- Find coordinates of points that divide line segments in various ratios

- Find solutions to inequalities represented by graphs or equations

- Write inequalities that fit given situations

- Solve systems of linear equations by graphing, by substituting, and by combining equations

- Choose strategically the most efficient solution method for a given system of linear equations

- Graph linear inequalities and systems of inequalities

- Describe the points that lie in regions determined by linear inequalities and systems of inequalities

- Use systems of linear equations and inequalities to solve problems

Developing Students' Mathematical Habits

The overall goal of the *Connected Mathematics* (CMP) curriculum is to help students develop sound mathematical habits. Through their work in this unit, students should ask themselves questions about situations that involve algebra, such as:

- *What patterns relate the coordinates of points on lines and curves?*

- *Does the problem involve an equation or an inequality?*

- *Does the problem call for writing and/or solving a system of equations? If so, what method would be useful for solving the system?*

- *What patterns relate the points whose coordinates satisfy linear equations?*

- *Are there systematic methods that can be used to solve any systems of linear equations?*

Overview

Algebraic ideas and techniques are powerful tools for reasoning about geometric shapes on a coordinate grid. Conversely, geometric images are useful aids to algebraic reasoning about linear equations and inequalities. This unit is designed to capitalize on the strong connections between algebra and geometry in order to extend students' understanding and skill in several significant aspects of those two key strands in the middle grades curriculum.

Circles, triangles, rectangles, and general parallelograms are visually familiar shapes. When those shapes are drawn on a coordinate grid, the coordinates of points comprising the figures can be identified as solutions for equations. The special geometric relationships that characterize various figures can be described and analyzed by studying properties of the corresponding equations.

For instance, points on a circle with center at the origin and radius r will have coordinates satisfying the equation:

$$x^2 + y^2 = r^2.$$

Points on (non-vertical) sides of any polygon will have coordinates satisfying linear equations of the form:

$$y = mx + b.$$

The coefficient m indicates the slope of the line, so parallel sides have the same slope and perpendicular sides have slopes with product -1.

Reasoning in the opposite direction—from geometry to algebra—the relationship between linear functions and straight-line graphs is helpful in understanding solution possibilities for systems of linear equations. If two lines such as $3x + 2y = 5$ and $3x + 2y = 7$ are parallel but disjoint, the corresponding system of linear equations will have no solutions. If the lines intersect in a single point, as do $x + 2y = 4$ and $-x + 3y = 6$, which meet only at $(0, 2)$, the corresponding system will have a unique solution.

When problem conditions suggest constraints represented by linear inequalities in two variables such as $3x + 2y < 5$ or $3x + 2y > 7$, the graphic representation becomes a half plane with many solutions.

These are the key ideas developed by problems in *The Shapes of Algebra* unit. They extend earlier work with the Pythagorean Theorem by connecting it to the standard equation for circles; with properties of polygons by connecting parallel and perpendicular lines to slopes of lines and linear functions; and with solutions of linear equations by considering solutions of linear systems and equations in standard $ax + by = c$ form, and solutions of linear inequalities.

These topics are standard parts of traditional Algebra I syllabi and they are included in many standard algebra examinations. However, the *Connected Mathematics* approach to the topics exploits the rich connections between algebra and geometry to strengthen student understanding of problems and solution methods that are often taught and learned in quite formal and rote ways. Since students who proceed to mathematically oriented academic specialties will undoubtedly study these topics in greater detail in high school mathematics, it is important to develop the sort of conceptual understanding that will provide a solid base for future work, not simply to settle for short-term rote learning of procedures that will be quickly forgotten.

Summary of Investigations

Investigation 1

Equations for Circles and Polygons

The main goal of this investigation is to begin to explore the geometry of the coordinate plane. The set of three problems uses the geometry of crop circle designs to pique student interest in use of coordinates and algebraic equations to describe geometric shapes. When one looks at the fantastic crop circle designs that have been created and impressed on fields all over the world, it is impossible to imagine that this work was done freehand and without use of coordinate locators and equations.

The equation for a circle, midpoints of lines, and parallel and perpendicular lines are explored in this investigation.

Investigation 2

Linear Equations and Inequalities

The main goal of this investigation is to lay out informal and graphic foundations for dealing with systems of linear equations in two variables. It reverses the geometry–algebra connection story line by beginning with algebraic expressions and using geometry to picture the conditions implied. It also focuses on equations in the $y = mx + b$ form and inequalities, $ax + b < cx + d$.

Investigation 3

Equations With Two or More Variables

The main goal of this investigation is to focus attention on what is curiously referred to as *standard form* $(ax + by = c)$ of linear equations, their graphs, and the geometric interpretation of solving a system of such equations. The investigation lays a visual foundation for the more algorithmic methods of solving linear systems that are addressed in Investigation 4. Students use graphical methods to solve systems of linear equations in standard form, or they can solve for y in each equation and set the two resulting equations equal.

Investigation 4

Solving Systems of Linear Equations Symbolically

The aim of this investigation is to develop understanding and skill in use of several standard strategies for finding solutions by algebraic reasoning, such as solving a system of linear equations by substitution or by combining equations.

Investigation 5

Linear Inequalities

This investigation develops some of the basic techniques for work with linear inequalities in the form $ax + by < c$ and $ax + by > c$. It does so in the context of problems that continue the unit perspective on connecting algebraic ideas to geometric shapes by emphasizing the connection between linear inequalities and the half-planes that are their graphs.

Mathematics Background

There are several key mathematical concepts developed in this unit.

Equations of Circles

To find the distance between two points where the line segment connecting the points is neither horizontal nor vertical, it is possible to treat the line segment as the hypotenuse of a right triangle. Problems like these were done in the unit *Looking for Pythagoras*. You can find the length of the hypotenuse—and thus the distance between the points—using the Pythagorean Theorem.

The following is a formula for finding the distance between two points,(x_1, y_1) and (x_2, y_2) in the plane:

$$d = \sqrt{\left(x_1 - x_2\right)^2 + \left(y_1 - y_2\right)^2}$$

The distance formula is simply a different form of the Pythagorean Theorem, $a^2 + b^2 = c^2$. In this case, leg a is the horizontal distance between the points $x_1 - x_2$. Leg b is the vertical distance between the points $y_1 - y_2$. The hypotenuse is the distance we seek. Thus, $a^2 + b^2 = c^2$ becomes: $(x_1 - x_2)^2 + (y_1 - y_2)^2 = d^2$.

Taking the square root of both sides yields the distance formula

$$\sqrt{\left(x_1 - x_2\right)^2 + \left(y_1 - y_2\right)^2} = d$$

Since the distance formula is an application of the Pythagorean theorem, either formula can be used to determine the equation for a circle. The use of each formula is explained below.

A circle can be defined as the set of points a given distance from a fixed point, called the center. When a circle of radius r is drawn on a coordinate grid with center at the origin (see Figure A), any point on the circle (x, y) can be viewed as a vertex of a right triangle with legs of length x and y and hypotenuse of length r (see Figure B). The Pythagorean Theorem says that for right triangles, $a^2 + b^2 = c^2$, where a and b are the legs of the right triangle and c is the hypotenuse. Applying the Pythagorean Theorem to the right triangle drawn in Figure A, we have $x^2 + y^2 = r^2$. This equation would be true for any point (x, y) on the circle in Figure A. So the equation represents the relationship for all points on the circle.

Figure A

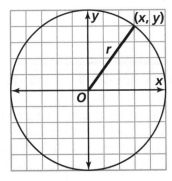

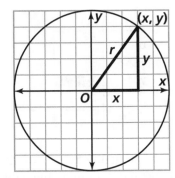

For circles centered at points other than the origin, such as (a, b), we compensate for the shift from the origin, and the equation becomes $(x - a)^2 + (y - b)^2 = r^2$.

We do not expect this level of generality from students in this unit.

The more general equation for a circle can also be generated from the distance formula. Using the distance formula, the distance from the center (a, b) to a point (x, y) on the circle is:

$$r = \sqrt{\left(x - a\right)^2 + \left(y - b\right)^2}$$

where r is radius of the circle. Squaring both sides of the equation yields:

$$r^2 = (x - a)^2 + (y - b)^2$$

Linear Inequalities

Eighth-grade *Connected Mathematics* students will have spent considerable time working with coordinate graphs of linear equations in the form $y = mx + b$ and their connection to the solution of linear equations such as $5x + 7 = 42$. What they will have spent much less time with is solution of linear inequalities such as $5x + 7 \leq 42$ and interpretation of those solutions on number line graphs or coordinate graphs.

There are three basic ways to look at such inequality problems. However, the first two, symbolically and graphically, are the primary ways that inequalities are mathematically solved. The inequality $5x + 7 \leq 42$ will be used to illustrate the three ways to solve an equality.

The first way is to solve the inequality symbolically through operations much like those used to solve linear equations:

$$5x + 7 \leq 42$$
$$5x \leq 35$$
$$x \leq 7$$

This method is similar to that of solving the equation $5x + 7 = 42$ symbolically in that operations (addition, subtraction, division, and multiplication) are applied to both sides of the inequality. However, when solving linear inequalities, students need to learn some special properties governing manipulation of those inequalities into equivalent (generally simpler) forms. With one exception, the rules for operations with inequalities are identical to those for operations with equations. The exception is that when one multiplies (or divides) both sides of an inequality by a negative number, the direction of the inequality is reversed. For example, the solution of the inequality $-5x + 7 \leq 42$ could proceed as follows and thus require a reverse in the direction of the inequality sign:

$$-5x + 7 \leq 42$$
$$-5x \leq 35$$
$$x \geq -7$$

To see why the direction of the inequality sign is reversed you can think of the positive and negative numbers arranged as mirror images around zero on a number line. Thus, 5 is to the left of 10, but -5 is to the right of -10. (Figure 1)

Figure 1

Any multiplication or division by a negative quantity will change the positive quantities to negative quantities, or vice versa, therefore the order of the quantities will be reversed. Thus $5 < 10$, but dividing the inequality by -1, you get $-10 < -5$.

Notice that you could proceed by adding $5x$ to both sides of the inequality as shown below and avoid the need to reverse the sign:

$$-5x + 7 \leq 42$$
$$7 \leq 42 + 5x$$
$$-35 \leq 5x$$
$$-7 \leq x$$

The second way to approach solving an inequality such as $5x + 7 \leq 42$ is graphically. Each side of the inequality is graphed as a function, i.e., $y = 5x + 7$ and $y = 42$. Note that the intersection of these two lines satisfies the equation $5x + 7 = 42$ and occurs when $x = 7$. However, we need to find when $5x + 7 \leq 42$. The points on the line $y = 5x + 7$ satisfying the condition that the y-coordinate is less than 42 are all the points on the bolded part of the line shown below. Since the original inequality is asking just for the x-values of these points, the solutions are the x-values corresponding to the points on this bolded section of the line $y = 5x + 7$. That is, the x-values for these points all have values that are less than or equal to 7. This solution is illustrated on the x-axis in the following diagram.

When examining the graph below ask yourself:

- *What values of x substituted into y = 5x + 7 give a value of y ≤ 42?*

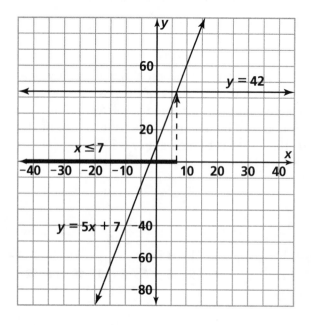

Another way to show this solution graphically is to represent only the x-axis as a number line. The graph would look like this:

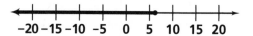

A third way to approach solving an inequality such as $5x + 7 \leq 42$ is by examining a table of values for the equation $y = 5x + 7$ using a graphing calculator like the one shown below:

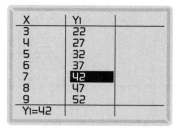

To solve the inequality $5x + 7 \leq 42$, examine the table above and determine the values of x for which the y-value is less than or equal to 42. As you can see from the table, the solution is $x \leq 7$.

Systems of Linear Equations

One of the standard topics in elementary algebra is the variety of techniques available for solving systems of two linear equations in two unknowns. *Connected Mathematics* students meet the early and simplest forms of such problems in the *Moving Straight Ahead* unit, in which they are asked to find intersection points of graphs for equations such as $y = 3x + 5$ and $y = 2x - 1$. This solution task can be handled fairly directly by realizing that the condition implies that $3x + 5 = 2x - 1$ and proceeding to a solution with methods that are applicable to linear equations in one unknown ($x = -6$ and thus $y = -13$).

Many problems that involve conditions on two variables are most naturally represented by pairs of equations in the form "$ax + by = c$ and $dx + ey = f$." There are several key ideas involved in working effectively with such systems. The first is the fact that if you plot all points with coordinates (x, y) satisfying an equation such as $3x + 5y = 8$, the graph will be a straight line. With a system of two such equations, there are three possible graphic results and, as a consequence, three solution possibilities.

Equations in the system

$$\begin{cases} 3x + 5y = 8 \\ 6x + y = 7 \end{cases}$$

will have graphs that intersect in a single point (1, 1). Thus the solution to the system is unique: $x = 1$ and $y = 1$.

Equations in the system

$$\begin{cases} 3x + 5y = 8 \\ 6x + 10y = 15 \end{cases}$$

will have parallel line graphs. Thus the solution set for the system of equations is empty.

Equations in the system

$$\begin{cases} 3x + 5y = 8 \\ 6x + 10y = 16 \end{cases}$$

will have identical graphs. Thus the solution set for the system is all (x, y) satisfying either equation, an infinite solution set.

There are three standard solution strategies for systems in the form just illustrated (other than the graphic solution, which we have used previously). Each has importance in later mathematical work, so conceptual understanding will be a useful foundation to build.

Graphic Solution of Systems The graphic method involves producing straight-line graphs for each equation and then reading coordinates of intersection points as the solution(s). Since this method relies on pictorial representation of the equations, coordinates of the intersection point can only be estimated and may not even appear in the graphing window chosen for display of the linear graphs. Thus it is important to check estimated solutions in the original equations and to verify that lines suspected of being parallel are actually parallel by checking slopes.

Equivalent Form When the equations in a system are given in $ax + by = c$ form, they can always be changed to $y = ax + b$ form. When the arithmetic is easy, this is a good strategy. For example,

$$\begin{cases} 2x + y = 5 \\ 9x - 3y = 15 \end{cases}$$

is the same as

$$\begin{cases} y = -2x + 5 \\ y = 3x - 5 \end{cases}$$

Now graphing the system is easy. But, also setting the two expressions for y equal eliminates a variable and gives $-2x + 5 = 3x - 5$. This gives $5x = 10$ or $x = 2$ and $y = 1$.

Solving Systems by Substitution A second method of solving linear systems is useful when one of the given equations can be easily rewritten in a form showing one variable as a function of the other. For example, in the system

$$\begin{cases} 3x + 5y = 8 \\ 6x + y = 7 \end{cases}$$

the second equation can be rewritten as $y = 7 - 6x$. Using this information about y and the first equation condition reveals that any solution must satisfy the condition $3x + 5(7 - 6x) = 8$. This equation with one unknown can be solved readily with methods from earlier work on linear equations to reveal $x = 1$ and then $y = 7 - 6(1)$ or $y = 1$.

This solution strategy is generally referred to as solution by substitution because of the way one variable is replaced by a substitute, equivalent expression (in this case, y is replaced by the expression $7 - 6x$). The substitution strategy turns out to be useful in solving a variety of other kinds of algebraic system problems.

Solving Systems by Linear Combination A third method of solving linear systems relies on two basic principles:

1. The solutions to any linear equation $ax + by = c$ are identical to the solutions of the equation $kax + kby = kc$. That is, multiplying both sides of a linear equation by the same (non-zero) number does not change the set of solutions. $kax + kby = kc$ is equivalent to $ax + by = c$.

2. The solution of any system of linear equations is unchanged if one of the equations is replaced by a new equation formed by adding the two original equations.

A consequence of these rules is that the sum of two distinct, non-parallel linear equations will be an equation that is satisfied by the solution to the original system. Consider a simple example. The system

$$\begin{cases} x = 5 \\ y = 10 \end{cases}$$

has the solution $(5, 10)$. If we add the equations, we get $x + y = 15$. This new equation shares the solution to the original system, $(5, 10)$. The three lines are on the graph below, all crossing at the point $(5, 10)$.

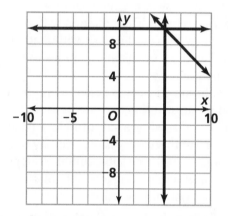

Because any combination (created by multiplying one or both equations by a constant and adding equations) will share the common solution to the original system, we can be strategic about seeking special combinations. In particular, if we can find a combination in only one variable, we will have found the value of this variable for the solution of the system and can compute the value of the other variable. This is what happens in the example in the Getting Ready questions. The system:

$$\begin{cases} x - y = 4 \\ x + y = 5 \end{cases}$$

yields the combination $2x = 9$, which is equivalent to $x = 4.5$. On the graph, we have the two original lines and the new, vertical line all going through the point $(4.5, 0.5)$.

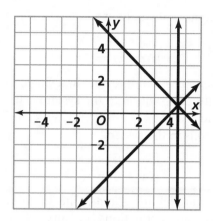

Since the applicability of these principles to the strategy of solving systems by linear combination is not intuitively obvious, this problem again uses the instructional technique of studying worked examples to present the strategy and get students thinking about what is involved.

Another example: solving the system

$$\begin{cases} 3x + 5y = 8 \\ 6x + y = 7 \end{cases}$$

by linear combinations might proceed something like this:

$$\begin{cases} 3x + 5y = 8 \\ 6x + y = 7 \end{cases}$$

(using Principle 1 to replace the first equation)

$$\begin{cases} -6x - 10y = -16 \\ 6x + y = 7 \end{cases}$$

(using Principle 2 to add the equations and replace the first equation)

$$\begin{cases} -9y = -9 \\ 6x + y = 7 \end{cases}$$

from which one can see that $y = 1$ and then that $x = 1$ by using the second equation.

As a general rule, use of the linear combinations method for solving systems requires some numerical intuition to select and use an efficient choice of combination operations. There are systematic algorithms that take the intuition out of the process, and those algorithms are available on most computer mathematics packages. However, the systematic linear combination procedures often involve complicated fraction calculations that will trip all but the very best human calculators! Thus the important goal for treatment of linear combinations in this unit is to lay an informal intuition about the key ideas involved, not to develop extremely high levels of proficiency in implementing the strategy.

Types of Solutions

When solving a system of two linear equations symbolically using the substitution or elimination methods described above, there are also the cases to consider where there is no solution there are infinitely many solutions.

Here are two examples. The first is:

$$\begin{cases} 6x + 3y = 9 \\ 4x + 2y = 7 \end{cases}$$

We can transform the first equation to become:

$$3y = -6x + 9 \text{ or } y = -2x + 3.$$

Substituting this into the second equation gives:

$$4x + 2(-2x + 3) = 7.$$

This simplifies to:

$$6 = 7.$$

Since the variable x has disappeared and the equation remaining ($6 = 7$) is not a true statement, no matter what value we assign to x, the solution to this system is the empty set. That is, since no value of x will make $6 = 7$ true, then no value of x will make the original system true; the two equations must not have a common solution.

Connecting to the graphical method for solving this system, this solution (the empty set or no solution) makes sense because both equations have slope -2. This verifies that their graphs are parallel and do not intersect.

The second example is

$$\begin{cases} 6x + 3y = 9 \\ 4x + 2y = 6 \end{cases}$$

Again, we can obtain $y = -2x + 3$ from the first equation. Substituting this into the second equation gives:

$$4x + 2(-2x + 3) = 6$$

This simplifies to:

$$6 = 6$$

Since the variable x has disappeared and the equation remaining ($6 = 6$) is true no matter what value we assign to x, the solution to the system is the set of all points that satisfy either of the original equations. This is a line. In this case, it is easy to verify that the original second equation

can be obtained from the first by multiplying each side of the first equation by $\frac{2}{3}$. Connecting to the graphical method for solving this system, this solution (the set of points that lie on one of the lines) makes sense because both equations simplify to the same equation $y = -2x + 3$ and thus represent the same line and contain all the same points. Thus, the set of points that satisfy the system is infinite.

Solving Linear Inequalities in Two Variables

In practical problem situations where linear conditions constrain the variables, realistic models of the problem conditions are often most naturally expressed by linear inequalities such as

$$ax + by < c$$

or

$$ax + by > c$$

rather than by equations. In these cases, the set of solutions (x, y) correspond to points in half of the coordinate plane rather than simply points on a single line. The only practical way to represent such solution sets is with a coordinate diagram. Shading the half-plane of interest is the standard notational convention.

The basic strategy that works well for graphing solutions of linear inequalities like $ax + by < c$ is to graph the boundary line $ax + by = c$ and then check points on either side of that boundary to see which satisfy the inequality condition. In many cases, the easiest point to check is $(0, 0)$.

Solving Systems of Linear Inequalities

In contrast to systems of equations, systems of inequalities tend to have infinite solution sets as well (that is, when the solution sets are not empty). The solution to a system of linear equations is the intersection of two lines. If the lines are distinct and not parallel, the intersection is a single point. The solution to a system of distinct, non-disjoint linear inequalities is the intersection of two half-planes, which contains infinitely many points.

In general, there are four regions suggested by a system of linear inequalities such as

$$\begin{cases} y < x \\ y > 2x - 5 \end{cases}$$

These regions are numbered 1–4 in the diagram below. Region 1 contains the solutions to the system, for all of the points satisfy both inequalities. Regions 2 and 3 contain points that satisfy one or the other, but not both of the inequalities. These points are not solutions to the system, although each point is a solution to one of the inequalities. Region 4 contains points that satisfy neither of the equations. These points are also not solutions to the system.

The convention is to show the boundaries of the region containing the solutions as broken lines if the inequality indicates strictly less than or strictly greater than, and to use solid lines for boundaries when the inequalities indicate less than *or equal to* or greater than *or equal to*.

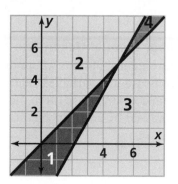

Big Idea	Prior Work	Future Work
Understanding the geometry of the coordinate plane: circles, parallel and perpendicular lines, and line segments	Thinking about shapes (*Shapes and Designs; Covering and Surrounding*) Working with coordinates (*Variables and Patterns; Moving Straight Ahead; Thinking With Mathematical Models; Looking for Pythagoras*) Finding midpoints of line segments (*Kaleidoscopes, Hubcaps, and Mirrors*)	Advanced algebra, geometry, and calculus
Using inequalities to interpret and represent situations	Formulating, reading, and interpreting symbolic rules (*Variables and Patterns; Moving Straight Ahead; Thinking With Mathematical Models; Accentuate the Negative*) Working with the triangle inequality (*Shapes and Designs; Looking for Pythagoras*)	Advanced algebra, calculus, and mathematical analysis
Developing graphical representations of inequalities	Solving problems in geometric and algebraic contexts (*Shapes and Designs; Moving Straight Ahead; Thinking With Mathematical Models; Accentuate the Negative*)	Calculus, advanced algebra
Writing and solving systems of linear equations	Solving linear equations (*Moving Straight Ahead; Thinking With Mathematical Models; Say it With Symbols*)	Advanced algebra and calculus

Pacing Suggestions and Materials

Investigations and Assessments	Pacing 45–50 min. classes	Materials for Students	Materials for Teachers
1 Equations for Circles and Polygons	5 days	graph paper, Labsheet 1.2 (1 per student)	Transparencies 1.1A–C, 1.2A, 1.2B, 1.3A–C
Mathematical Reflections	$\frac{1}{2}$ day		
2 Linear Equations and Inequalities	4 days	graph paper	Transparencies 2.1A, 2.1B, 2.2, 2.3A, 2.3B
Mathematical Reflections	$\frac{1}{2}$ day		
Assessment: Check Up 1	1 day		
3 Equations With Two or More Variables	4 days	graph paper, Labsheet 3.1 (1 per group), Labsheet 3.3 (1 per group)	Transparencies 3.1A, 3.1B, 3.2A, 3.2B, 3.3
Mathematical Reflections	$\frac{1}{2}$ day		
Assessment: Quiz	1 day		
4 Solving Systems of Linear Equations Symbolically	$5\frac{1}{2}$ days	graph paper	Poster paper (optional), Transparencies 4.1A, 4.1B, 4.2, 4.3A, 4.3B, 4.4
Mathematical Reflections	$\frac{1}{2}$ day		
5 Linear Inequalities	5 days	graph paper, Labsheet 5.1 (1 per pair)	Transparencies 5.1A, 5.1B, 5.2, 5.3A–D, 5.4
Mathematical Reflections	$\frac{1}{2}$ day		
Looking Back and Looking Ahead	1 day		
Assessment: Self Assessment	Take Home		
Assessment: Unit Test	1 day		

Total Time 30 days	**Materials for Use in All Investigations**	
For detailed pacing for Problems within each Investigation, see the Suggested Pacing at the beginning of each investigation.	Graphing calculators, blank transparencies and transparency markers (optional), student notebooks	Blank transparencies and transparency markers (optional)
For pacing with block scheduling, see next page.		

Pacing for Block Scheduling (90-minute class periods)

Investigation	Suggested Pacing	Investigation	Suggested Pacing	Investigation	Suggested Pacing
Investigation 1	**3 days**	**Investigation 3**	**$2\frac{1}{2}$ days**	**Investigation 5**	**$2\frac{1}{2}$ days**
Problem 1.1	1 day	Problem 3.1	$\frac{1}{2}$ day	Problem 5.1	$\frac{1}{2}$ day
Problem 1.2	$\frac{1}{2}$ day	Problem 3.2	$\frac{1}{2}$ day	Problem 5.2	$\frac{1}{2}$ day
Problem 1.3	1 day	Problem 3.3	1 day	Problem 5.3	$\frac{1}{2}$ day
Math Reflections	$\frac{1}{2}$ day	Math Reflections	$\frac{1}{2}$ day	Problem 5.4	1 day
Investigation 2	**$2\frac{1}{2}$ days**	**Investigation 4**	**4 days**	Math Reflections	$\frac{1}{2}$ day
Problem 2.1	$\frac{1}{2}$ day	Problem 4.1	1 day		
Problem 2.2	$\frac{1}{2}$ day	Problem 4.2	1 day		
Problem 2.3	1 day	Problem 4.3	$\frac{1}{2}$ day		
Math Reflections	$\frac{1}{2}$ day	Problem 4.4	1 day		
		Math Reflections	$\frac{1}{2}$ day		

Vocabulary

Essential Terms Developed in This Unit	Useful Terms Referenced in This Unit	Terms Developed in Previous Units	
Combination method	Estimate	Circles	Parallel
Inequality	Justify	Coordinates	Parallelogram
Standard form of a linear equation	Strategy	Costs	Perpendicular
Substitution method		Endpoint	Polygons
System of linear equations		Equations	Profit
System of linear inequalities		Equivalent equations	Quadratic Functions
		Equivalent expressions	Radius
		Exponential functions	Rectangle
		Inequality	Slope
		Linear functions	Vertex
		Line segment	x-intercept
		Midpoint	y-intercept

Program Resources

Go Online PHSchool.com

For: Teacher Resources
Web Code: apk-5500

Components

Use the chart below to quickly see which components are available for each Investigation.

Invest.	Labsheets	Additional Practice	Transparencies		Formal Assessment		Assessment Options	
			Problem	Summary	Check Up	Partner Quiz	Multiple-Choice	Question Bank
1	Labsheet 1.2, Labsheet 1ACE Exercises 3 and 4	✔	1.1A–C, 1.2A, 1.2B, 1.3A, 1.3B				✔	✔
2		✔	2.1A, 2.1B, 2.2, 2.3A, 2.3B		✔		✔	✔
3	Labsheets 3.1, 3.3	✔	3.1A–C, 3.2A, 3.2B, 3.3			✔	✔	✔
4		✔	4.1A, 4.1B, 4.2, 4.3				✔	✔
5	Labsheets 5.1	✔	5.1A, 5.1B, 5.2, 5.3A–D, 5.4				✔	✔
For the Unit		*ExamView* CD-ROM, Web site	LBLA		Unit Test, Notebook Check, Self Assessment		Multiple-Choice, Question Bank, *ExamView* CD-ROM	

Also Available for Use With This Unit
- Parent Guide: take-home letter for the unit
- Implementing CMP
- Spanish Assessment Resources
- Additional online and technology resources

Technology

The Use of Calculators

Connected Mathematics was developed with the belief that calculators should be available and that students should learn when their use is appropriate. For this reason, we do not designate specific problems as "calculator problems." However . . .

Student Activity CD-ROM

Includes interactive activities to enhance the learning in the Problems within Investigations.

PHSchool.com

For Students Multiple-choice practice with instant feedback, updated data sources, data sets for TinkerPlots™ data software.

For Teachers Professional development, curriculum support, downloadable forms, and more.

See also www.math.msu.edu/cmp for more resources for both teachers and students.

ExamView® CD-ROM

Create multiple versions of practice sheets and tests for course objectives and standardized tests. Includes dynamic questions, online testing, student reports, and all test and practice items in Spanish. Also includes all items in the Assessment Resources and Additional Practice.

TeacherExpress™ CD-ROM

Includes a lesson planning tool, the Teacher's Guide pages, and all the teaching resources.

LessonLab Online Courses

LessonLab offers comprehensive, facilitated professional development designed to help teachers implement CMP2 and improve student achievement. To learn more, please visit PHSchool.com/cmp2.

Assessment Summary

Ongoing Informal Assessment

Embedded in the Student Unit
Problems Use students' work from the Problems to check student understanding.

ACE Exercises Use ACE exercises for homework assignments to assess student understanding.

Mathematical Reflections Have students summarize their learning at the end of each Investigation.

Looking Back and Looking Ahead At the end of the unit, use the first two sections to allow students to show what they know about the unit.

Additional Resources
Teacher's Guide Use the Check for Understanding feature of some Summaries and the probing questions that appear in the *Launch, Explore,* or *Summarize* sections of all Investigations to check student understanding.

Self Assessment
Notebook Check Students use this tool to organize and check their notebooks before giving them to their teacher. Located in *Assessment Resources*.

Self Assessment At the end of the unit, students reflect on and provide examples of what they learned. Located in *Assessment Resources*.

Formal Assessment

Choose the assessment materials that are appropriate for your students.

Assessment	For Use After	Focus	Student Work
Check Up 1	Invest. 2	Skills	Individual
Partner Quiz	Invest. 3	Rich problems	Pair
Unit Test	The Unit	Skills, rich problems	Individual

Additional Resources
Multiple-Choice Items Use these items for homework, review, a quiz, or add them to the Unit Test.

Question Bank Choose from these questions for homework, review, or replacements for Quiz, Check Up, or Unit Test questions.

Additional Practice Choose practice exercises for each investigation for homework, review, or formal assessments.

***ExamView*® CD-ROM** Create practice sheets and review quizzes and tests with this dynamic software. Give online tests and receive student progress reports. (All test items available in Spanish.)

Spanish Assessment Resources
Includes Partner Quizzes, Check Ups, Unit Test, Multiple-Choice Items, Question Bank, Notebook Check, and Self Assessment. Plus, the *ExamView* CD-ROM has all test items in Spanish.

Correlation to Standardized Tests

Investigation	NAEP	Terra Nova CAT6	CTBS	ITBS	SAT10	Local Test
1 Equations for Circles and Polygons	A2c, A2d, G4d				✔	
2 Linear Equations and Inequalities	A2c, A2d, A4a, A4b	✔	✔	✔	✔	
3 Equations With Two or More Variables	A2a, A2b, A2c, A4d	✔			✔	
4 Solving Systems of Linear Equations Symbolically	A4b, A4c					
5 Linear Inequalities	A2c, A4a	✔				

NAEP National Assessment of Educational Progress

CAT6/Terra Nova California Achievement Test, 6th Ed.
CTBS/Terra Nova Comprehensive Test of Basic Skills

ITBS Iowa Test of Basic Skills, Form M
SAT10 Stanford Achievement Test, 10th Ed.

Introducing Your Students to *The Shapes of Algebra*

Previously, students have been solving equations using tables, graphs, or symbolic methods. Students were often asked informally to decide when two quantities were not equal or when one was less than the other. For example, to determine which rental company is less expensive, students might find when the cost of the two plans are equal using equations. Next, they might pick a value of the independent variable greater or less than the value where the two plans are equal and substitute that value into the equation to determine which plan costs less. In this unit they will develop more efficient methods for working with inequalities as well as with systems of linear equations.

Using the Unit Opener

The questions posed on the opening page of the Student Edition are designed to start students thinking about the kinds of questions and mathematics in the unit. Don't look for "correct" answers at this time. Do, however, present an opportunity for the class to discuss the questions and to start to think about what is needed to answer them. You may want to revisit these questions as students learn the mathematical ideas and techniques necessary to find the answers.

Using the Mathematical Highlights

The Mathematical Highlights page in the Student Edition provides information to students, parents, and other family members. It gives students a preview of the mathematics and some of the overarching questions that they should ask themselves while studying *The Shapes of Algebra*.

As they work through the unit, students can refer back to the Mathematical Highlights page to review what they have learned and to preview what is still to come. This page also tells students' families what mathematical ideas and activities will be covered as the class works through *The Shapes of Algebra*.

Connected Mathematics 2™

The Shapes of Algebra

Linear Systems and Inequalities

Glenda Lappan
James T. Fey
William M. Fitzgerald
Susan N. Friel
Elizabeth Difanis Phillips

PEARSON

Boston, Massachusetts · Glenview, Illinois · Shoreview, Minnesota · Upper Saddle River, New Jersey

Notes _____

_____

_____

_____

(1) 16

The Shapes of Algebra

Linear Systems and Inequalities

How do you think you might use equations, graphs, and properties of geometric figures to make crop designs like those that have appeared over the past 20 years in farmer's fields?

Some eighth-graders hope to raise $600 with a fundraiser. They will earn a profit of $5 for every T-shirt sold and $10 for every cap. What are some ways they can exactly reach the goal of $600?

A family wants to drive their car and SUV no more than 1,000 miles a month. They also want to limit total CO_2 emissions to less than 600 pounds. The car emits 0.75 pounds of CO_2 per mile, and the SUV emits 1.25 pounds. What are some *(car miles, SUV miles)* pairs that meet these conditions?

2   The Shapes of Algebra

Notes _____

_____

_____

_____

In *The Shapes of Algebra*, you will apply and extend what you've learned about properties of polygons, symmetry, the Pythagorean Theorem, linear equations, slope, and solution methods for equations and inequalities.

You will connect geometry and algebra as you investigate geometric figures on coordinate grids and write equations and inequalities to describe the boundaries and interiors of those figures. You will write linear and quadratic equations whose solutions indicate coordinates of key points on quadrilaterals, triangles, and circles. You will also use inequalities to describe points in regions of the coordinate plane.

You will model problems like those on the previous page by writing systems of linear equations and inequalities. The methods for solving these systems combine geometric and algebraic reasoning.

Notes _____

_____

_____

_____

Mathematical Highlights

Linear Systems and Inequalities

In *The Shapes of Algebra,* you will explore the relationship between algebra and geometry. Through this exploration, you will work with equations for lines and curves, and will develop an understanding of how systems of equations and inequalities can help you solve problems.

You will learn how to

- Write and use equations of circles
- Determine if lines are parallel or perpendicular by looking at patterns in their graphs, coordinates, and equations
- Find coordinates of points that divide line segments in various ratios
- Find solutions to inequalities represented by graphs or equations
- Write inequalities that fit given conditions
- Solve systems of linear equations by graphing, by substituting, and by combining equations
- Choose strategically the most efficient solution method for a given system of linear equations
- Graph linear inequalities and systems of inequalities
- Describe the points that lie in regions determined by linear inequalities and systems of inequalities
- Use systems of linear equations and inequalities to solve problems

As you work on problems in this unit, ask yourself questions like these:

What patterns relate the coordinates of points on lines and curves?

What patterns relate the points whose coordinates satisfy linear equations?

Does the problem involve an equation or an inequality?

Does the problem call for writing and/or solving a system of equations? If so, what method would be useful for solving the system?

Are there systematic methods that can be used to solve any systems of linear equations?

4 The Shapes of Algebra

Notes _____

_____

_____

_____

Investigation 1 — Equations for Circles and Polygons

Mathematical and Problem-Solving Goals

- Find equations describing coordinates for points on circles centered at the origin
- Use inequalities to describe points in the interior of a circle
- Use coordinates of vertices and equations to identify and describe parallel and perpendicular lines and midpoints of segments
- Describe parallelograms and rectangles on a coordinate grid

The main goal of this investigation is to begin exploration of the geometry of the coordinate plane. The three problems use the geometry of crop circle designs to pique student interest in use of coordinates and algebraic equations to describe geometric shapes. When one looks at the interesting crop circle designs that have been created and impressed on fields all over the world, it is impossible to imagine that this work was done freehand and without use of coordinate locators and equations.

Summary of Problems

Problem 1.1 Equations for Circles

Begins by asking students to think about patterns of coordinates for points on and inside of circles. The problem deals only with the case of circles centered at the origin of a coordinate system and uses the Pythagorean Theorem to lead to a general formula $x^2 + y^2 = r^2$. To give interior points, we write $x^2 + y^2 < r^2$.

Problem 1.2 Parallels and Perpendiculars

Explores patterns in coordinates of points that determine parallelograms and rectangles. To start the exploration, students look at crop circle designs made of polygons inscribed in circles in various ways. Students construct rectangles and parallelograms on a coordinate grid, find the equations for the sides of those figures, and connect geometric slope to equations. The result should be a reminder that parallel lines have the same slope and perpendicular lines have slopes that are inverse reciprocals of each other. This should connect with and extend work in the *Looking for Pythagoras* unit done earlier.

Problem 1.3 Finding Midpoints

Focuses on the special properties of midpoints and lines that connect them in quadrilaterals. Students establish the beautiful result that the figure formed by connecting (in order) midpoints of sides of any quadrilateral is a parallelogram.

	Suggested Pacing	Materials for Students	Materials for Teachers	ACE Assignments
All	5 days	graph paper		
1.1	$1\frac{1}{2}$ days		Transparencies 1.1A–C	1–2, 24–46, 60, 61
1.2	$1\frac{1}{2}$ days	Labsheet 1.2 (one per student), Labsheet 1ACE Exercises 3 and 4	Transparencies 1.2A, 1.2B	3–16, 47–51
1.3	$1\frac{1}{2}$ days		Transparencies 1.3A–C	17–23, 52–59, 62–66
MR	$\frac{1}{2}$ day			

1.1 Equations for Circles

Goals

- Find equations describing coordinates for points on circles centered at the origin
- Find inequalities describing coordinates of points in the interior of a circle

Launch 1.1

Talk about the crop circle design shown in the introduction to the investigation. Ask students how they would make a plan for creating their own crop circles. Talk to students about the Getting Ready. You might use images from a website devoted to crop circles to launch this problem.

Suggested Questions

- *Suppose you are planning to make a crop circle design like the one shown. How can you outline the circle accurately?* (Answers will probably vary. One possibility is to make a scale drawing. The drawing could be made on a coordinate grid for convenience of describing the shapes in the drawing.)

To draw the circle, students might suggest use of various tools like compasses, tracing circular shapes, or using a string with one end fixed at the center of the circle.

- *How can you locate sides and vertices of the other shapes in the design?*
- *How can you use equations and coordinate graphs to help plan your design?*

At this point students might not have any very well-formed ideas about this question. They might want to use coordinates for the vertices of the triangles, but it is unlikely that they will have ideas about coordinate equations of circles.

You might talk with students about how much easier a coordinate graph could make the drawing, particularly if you could find equations to describe the circle and other components of the design.

Suggested Questions

- *If you knew the center and the radius of a circle, how could you outline that circle in a field?* (You could anchor a rope and walk around the anchor. The rope would keep you on a circular path. Of course, you'd have to keep the rope pretty high so that the cornstalks didn't get in the way!)

Look at the picture in the introduction to Problem 1.1.

- *Are there any points on this circle whose coordinates are easy to find?* (The coordinates on the axes are easier to find than others, because we know that one coordinate is 0.)
- *In this problem, we will look for mathematical ways to describe the coordinates of the other points on a circle located on a grid.*

Arrange students in groups of three or four.

Explore 1.1

In Question A, ask students if their answers are the only possible answers. Parts (1a)–(1h) have two answers each, but part (1i) has only one answer. You might have a quick whole-class discussion when students are nearly finished with Question A, before having them go on to Questions B–E.

In Question B, ask students to draw the right triangles for a couple of other locations for point (x, y).

Suggested Question

- *What happens to the sides of the right triangles as (x, y) travels around the circle?*

In Questions B and C, students may struggle with writing the equation relating the x- and y-coordinates of a circle. Let them try some ideas before intervening. Spend time on this idea in the summary.

You could do Question D as a whole class, once students have worked on Questions A–C.

Summarize 1.1

Work with students to identify how they can use the Pythagorean Theorem to write down the relationship $x^2 + y^2 = 5^2$. Once they see the relationship with a circle of radius 5, Question E should be simpler.

Be sure to get students to articulate their reasoning about how the length of the circle radius (5) is related to the x- and y-coordinates by the Pythagorean theorem.

Ask students to share the coordinates of points they found in the interior of the circle.

Suggested Questions

- *What do all of these points have in common?* (They all have coordinates satisfying inequalities such as $x > -5, x < 5, y > -5$, and $y < 5$.)

- *Is this a complete description of points in the interior of the circle?* [Not quite, because $(4.9, 4.9)$ is a point that has coordinates satisfying all of those inequalities, but it lies outside the circle. In fact, the four inequalities above would describe a square region enclosing the circle.]

- *Can we use a picture like the one before Question B to help describe these coordinates?* (Draw a picture like the following, including the point in the interior of the circle.)

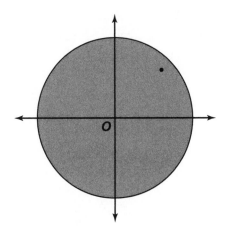

- *What paths can we draw from the origin to this point?* (The students may come up with a picture like the one below.)

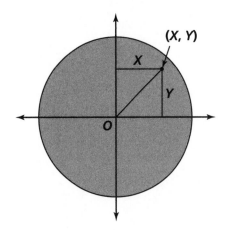

Point to the hypotenuse of the right triangles.

- *What do we know about this length?* (It's less than 5.)

- *How can we write an inequality describing all of the points in the interior of the circle?* ($x^2 + y^2 < 25$ or $\sqrt{x^2 + y^2} < 5$)

- *Why do we write a* less than *symbol instead of* less than or equal to? (Because a less than or equal to symbol would include the circle itself.)

1.1 Equations for Circles

Mathematical Goals

- Find equations describing coordinates for points on circles centered at the origin
- Find inequalities describing coordinates of points in the interior of a circle

Launch

Talk about the crop circle design in the introduction. Ask students how they would make a plan for making their own design. Discuss the Getting Ready.

Talk about how much easier a coordinate graph could make the drawing, particularly if you could find equations to describe the circle and other components of the design.

- *If you knew the center and the radius of a circle, how could you outline that circle in a field?*

Talk about the picture in the introduction to Problem 1.1.

- *Are there any points on this circle whose coordinates are easy to find? In this problem, we will look for mathematical ways to describe the coordinates of the other points on a circle located on a grid.*

Materials
- Transparencies 1.1A–C

Vocabulary
- circle

Explore

In Question A, ask students if their answers are the only possible answers. Parts (1a)–(1h) have two answers each, but part (1i) has only one answer. You might have a quick whole-class discussion when students are nearly finished with Question A before having them go on to Questions B–E.

In Questions B and C, students may struggle with writing the equation relating the x- and y-coordinates of a circle. Let them try some ideas before intervening. Spend time on this idea in the summary.

Summarize

Work with students to identify how they can use the Pythagorean Theorem to write down the relationship $x^2 + y^2 = 5^2$. Once they see the relationship with a circle of radius 5, Question E should be simpler.

Get students to articulate how the length of the circle radius (5) is related to the x- and y-coordinates by the Pythagorean Theorem.

Do Question D as a whole class and ask students to share the coordinates of points in the interior of the circle.

Materials
- Student notebooks

Vocabulary
- inequality

continued on next page

continued

Draw a circle centered at the origin including a point in the interior.

● *What paths can we draw from the origin to this point?*

Point to the hypotenuse of the right triangles.

● *What do we know about this length? How can we write an inequality describing all of the points in the interior of the circle?*

ACE Assignment Guide for Problem 1.1

Core 1–2, 24–27, 31–33, 35–46
Other *Applications* 28–30, 34, *Extensions* 60, 61, and unassigned choices from previous problems

Adapted For suggestions about adapting ACE exercises, see the CMP *Special Needs Handbook*.
Connecting to Prior Units 24–27: *Looking for Pythagoras*; 28–33: *Moving Straight Ahead*; 35–46: *Accentuate the Negative*; 34: *Kaleidoscopes, Hubcaps, and Mirrors*

Answers to Problem 1.1

A. 1. a. 5 or −5 **b.** 5 or −5 **c.** 4 or −4
  d. 3 or −3 **e.** 4 or −4 **f.** 3 or −3
  g. approximately 4.6 or −4.6;
    exactly $\pm\sqrt{21}$
  h. approximately 4.6 or −4.6;
    exactly $\pm\sqrt{21}$
  i. 0

  2. Problems a, b and i are exactly correct because the radius is 5.
  Problems c, d, e, and f are exactly correct because the coordinates form a 3, 4, 5 triangle, and using the Pythagorean theorem you could easily find the missing coordinate.

B. 1. Starting with the given picture, as the value of x approaches zero, the value of y increases. Then as x becomes negative, the value of y decreases.

  2. The right triangles become taller and thinner as x approaches zero, but then they again become shorter and wider as x approaches −5.

3. $x^2 + y^2 = 5^2$ or $x^2 + y^2 = 25$ are probably the most direct and natural ways of representing the Pythagorean relationship between x, y, and the radius 5.

4. Kaitlyn's equations work only for two positions of (x, y), such as $(0, 5)$ and $(5, 0)$. For example, consider $(3, 4)$. $4 \neq 5 - 3$.

5. Yes, since we can always make the right triangle unless we are on the axes, in which case $0^2 + 5^2 = 5^2$, etc.

C. 1. $3^2 + 4^2 = 5^2$;
    $3^2 + 4^2 = 9 + 16 = 25 = 5^2$

  2. $(-4)^2 + 3^2 = 5^2$;
    $(-4)^2 + 3^2 = 16 + 9 = 25 = 5^2$

  3. $(\sqrt{13})^2 + (\sqrt{12})^2 = 5^2$;
    $(\sqrt{13})^2 + (\sqrt{12})^2 = 13 + 12 = 25 = 5^2$

  4. $0^2 + (-5)^2 = 5^2$;
    $0^2 + (-5)^2 = 0 + 25 = 25 = 5^2$

  5. No, if we choose a point outside the circle then $x^2 + y^2 > 25$. The solutions of $x^2 + y^2 = 5^2$ are only points on the circle since (x, y) is 5 units from the center.

D. 1. Answers may vary, but possibilities are: $(2, 3), (1, 2)$ and $(0, 0)$.

  2. $x^2 + y^2 < 5^2$

E. $x^2 + y^2 = 1^2, x^2 + y^2 = 3^2, x^2 + y^2 = 10^2$

1.2 Parallels and Perpendiculars

Goals

- Construct special quadrilaterals on a coordinate grid

- Use slopes of parallel and perpendicular lines to reason about parallelograms and rectangles on coordinate grids

Launch 1.2

Have students look at the picture before Problem 1.2 and the diagram showing how this figure might be represented on a coordinate grid.

Suggested Questions

- *What are the vertices of the overlapping rectangles?*

Allow students to think about this for a moment. Answers will be *ABEF* and *BCFG* or some equivalent variation.

- *What kind of figure is HBDF?* (It appears to be a rhombus.)

- *What lines in the figure appear to be parallel? Which appear to be perpendicular?* (There are many possible pairs to mention. For example, $\overleftrightarrow{AF} \| \overleftrightarrow{BE}$, $\overleftrightarrow{AB} \| \overleftrightarrow{FE}$, and $\overleftrightarrow{AF} \perp \overleftrightarrow{FE}$)

- *In this problem, you will explore patterns relating parallel and perpendicular lines and their equations.*

Before arranging students in groups, you may want to divide up the work for Question E. All the groups can draw the corner coordinates in Question E, part (1), but finding all of the slopes is an unnecessary amount of work for any given student. Ask different groups to work on different rectangular shapes on the grid, and then collect the data from the whole class to help figure out patterns. Arrange students in groups of three or four.

Explore 1.2

Circulate as students work on the problem. Ask them how they justify their choices of coordinates in Question A. You may want to ask what kinds of conjectures students make about the lines in the picture. Although our exploration focuses on slope, students may also notice that symmetry plays a big role in looking at the *x*- and *y*-intercepts.

You'll probably want to have a whole-group discussion when all groups have completed Question C. Faster groups can go ahead to Question D, since it extends and applies results from Questions A–C.

Going Further

1. Find the coordinates of points *H* and *D*.

   [*D* $(0, -\frac{5}{3})$, *H* $(0, \frac{5}{3})$. To find points *D* and *H*, use the endpoints of the segments $\overline{EB}$ and $\overline{GB}$ to find the equations of the line segment through the points *E, B* and *D,* and *G, B* and *H,* respectively. The equation for the line through *E* $(-4, -3)$ and *B* $(5, 0)$ is $y = \frac{1}{3}x - \frac{5}{3}$. Thus the *y*-intercept of this line is $(0, -\frac{5}{3})$, which is also point *D.* The equation for the line through *G* $(-4, 3)$ and *B* $(5, 0)$ is $y = -\frac{1}{3}x + \frac{5}{3}$. Thus the *y*-intercept of this line is $(0, \frac{5}{3})$, which is also point *H.*]

2. Show that *FHBD* is a rhombus. (Use the Pythagorean Theorem to find the length of the 4 sides or use reflection symmetry.)

Summarize 1.2

Ask groups of students to show what corner coordinates for the rectangles they found. All points except *D* and *H* can be inferred rather easily by using symmetry arguments and the fact that points *B* and *F* are on the *x*-axis and the circle of radius 5. To find coordinates of *D* and *H* in the Going Further, students will need to do something like finding the equation of line $\overleftrightarrow{FA}$ (which is $y = \frac{1}{3}x + \frac{5}{3}$) and noticing that *H* is the *y*-intercept of that line $(0, \frac{5}{3})$.

Ask groups of students to share their slope data for Question B with each other—either among groups or in whole class presentations of work. Then ask about patterns in the slopes.

Suggested Questions

- *How would these patterns in Question B show up in equations for pairs of lines that are parallel?* (They would have the same slope. In other words, if we had two equations of lines, $y = mx + b$ and $y = nx + c$, m and n would be the same.)

The second pattern in Question C will be more difficult for students. You may need to organize the slopes in order to make the relationship more obvious, including writing 3 as an improper fraction $\left(\frac{3}{1}\right)$.

- *How would these patterns in Question C show up in equations for pairs of lines that are perpendicular?* (The slopes would be the negative reciprocal of each other. In other words, if we had two equations of lines, $y = mx + b$ and $y = nx + c$, then $mn = -1$.)

Ask for some examples from the groups for Question D. The main idea is to realize that as the point A (x, y) travels around the circle, each new location can be used to make a rectangle whose vertices are on the circle, except for the points where A lies on the x- or y-axis. Here the rectangle becomes a line or a square.

Question E can be assigned for homework because its purpose is to practice visualizing shapes and finding slopes and equations of lines.

1.2 Parallels and Perpendiculars

Mathematical Goals

- Construct special quadrilaterals on a coordinate grid
- Use slopes of parallel and perpendicular lines to reason about parallelograms and rectangles on coordinate grids

Launch

Have students look at the picture before Problem 1.2 and the diagram showing how this figure might be represented on a coordinate grid.

- *What are the vertices of the overlapping rectangles?*
- *What kind of figure is HBDF?*
- *What lines in the figure appear to be parallel? Which appear to be perpendicular?*

Before arranging students in groups, divide up the work for Question E. Finding all of the slopes is an unnecessary amount of work for any given student. Ask different groups to work on different rectangular shapes on the grid, and then collect the data from the whole class to help figure out patterns. Arrange students in groups of three or four.

Materials
- Transparencies 1.2A and 1.2B
- Labsheet 1.2

Vocabulary
- perpendicular lines
- parallelogram

Explore

Ask students to justify their choices of coordinates in Question A.

- *What kinds of conjectures are you making about the lines in the picture?*

Although our exploration focuses on slope, students may also notice that symmetry plays a big role in looking at the x- and y-intercepts.

Have a mid-problem summary after Question C.

Summarize

Ask groups of students to share their corner coordinates. All points except *D* and *H* can be inferred rather easily by using symmetry arguments and the fact that points *B* and *F* are on the x-axis and the circle of radius 5.

To find coordinates of *D* and *H*, students will need to find the equation of the line containing *D* and *H*.

Ask students to share their slope data from Question E—either among groups or in whole-class presentations.

- *How do these patterns show up in equations for pairs of parallel lines?*
- *How do these patterns show up in equations for pairs of perpendicular lines?*

The second pattern will be more difficult for students. You may need to organize the slopes in order to make the relationship more obvious, including writing 3 as an improper fraction $\left(\frac{3}{1}\right)$.

Materials
- Student notebooks

ACE Assignment Guide for Problem 1.2

Core 4–16, 49

Other *Applications* 3, *Connections* 47, 48, *Extensions* 50, 51 and unassigned choices from previous problems
Labsheet 1ACE Exercises 3 and 4 is provided if Exercises 3 and 4 are assigned.

Adapted For suggestions about adapting ACE exercises, see the CMP *Special Needs Handbook*.
Connecting to Prior Units 47: *Stretching and Shrinking*; 48: *Kaleidoscopes, Hubcaps, and Mirrors*; 49: *Moving Straight Ahead*; 50: *Stretching and Shrinking*; 51: *Data Distributions*

Answers to Problem 1.2

A. $B(5, 0)$, $C(4, -3)$, $E(-4, -3)$, $F(-5, 0)$, $G(-4, 3)$

B. $\overleftrightarrow{AF} \| \overleftrightarrow{BE}$ with common slope $\frac{1}{3}$;

$\overleftrightarrow{AB} \| \overleftrightarrow{FE}$ with common slope -3;

$\overleftrightarrow{GB} \| \overleftrightarrow{FC}$ with common slope $-\frac{1}{3}$;

$\overleftrightarrow{GF} \| \overleftrightarrow{BC}$ with common slope 3;

Slopes of parallel lines are the same. This makes sense because parallel lines travel along in the same direction, never meeting.

C. $\overleftrightarrow{AF} \perp \overleftrightarrow{AB}$, slopes are $\frac{1}{3}$ and -3

$\overleftrightarrow{BE} \perp \overleftrightarrow{FE}$, slopes are -3 and $\frac{1}{3}$

$\overleftrightarrow{BE} \perp \overleftrightarrow{AB}$, slopes are $\frac{1}{3}$ and -3

$\overleftrightarrow{AF} \perp \overleftrightarrow{EF}$, slopes are $\frac{1}{3}$ and -3

$\overleftrightarrow{BG} \perp \overleftrightarrow{CB}$, slopes are $-\frac{1}{3}$ and 3

$\overleftrightarrow{BC} \perp \overleftrightarrow{CF}$, slopes are 3 and $-\frac{1}{3}$

$\overleftrightarrow{CF} \perp \overleftrightarrow{FG}$, slopes are $-\frac{1}{3}$ and 3

$\overleftrightarrow{FG} \perp \overleftrightarrow{GB}$, slopes are 3 and $-\frac{1}{3}$

Note: In each case the slopes are negative reciprocals of each other (although, this principle might not be as obvious due to there being only 4 slopes in this part: $\pm\frac{1}{3}$ and ±3. You might wait until students have done Question D before you press for the standard result.

D. Yes; $(2, \sqrt{21})$, $(5, 0)$, $(-5, 0)$, and $(-2, -\sqrt{21})$.
$$2^2 + y^2 = 5^2$$
$$y^2 = 25 - 4$$
$$y^2 = 21$$
$$y = \sqrt{21}$$

E. 1.

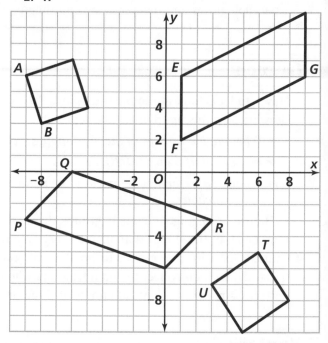

2. *ABCD*; *C* and *D* coordinates may vary, but for vertices with both coordinates integers, the possibilities are $C(-2, 5)$ and $D(-3, 8)$ or $C(-5, 4)$ and $D(-6, 7)$.
EFGH has $H(9, 10)$. *PQRS* has $S(0, -6)$. *TUVW* has $V(5, -10)$ and $W(8, -8)$ as the only possibility with integer coordinates that fit on the diagram and do not overlap another figure.

3. The slopes of parallel lines are the same.

4. The slopes of perpendicular lines are reciprocals of each other with opposite signs. Note that this means they multiply together to give -1.

5. Answers will vary, but some examples are: parallel lines: $y = mx + b$ and $y = mx + c$ (same slopes)
perpendicular lines: $y = mx + b$ and $y = (\frac{-1}{m})x + c$ (negative reciprocal slopes)

1.3 Finding Midpoints

Goals

- Find the midpoint of any given line segment
- Explore the special properties of figures determined by connecting midpoints of sides of quadrilaterals

Launch 1.3

Draw students' attention to the figure shown in the introduction to the problem and give them some time to think about how they would identify key points and segments in the figure by measuring or folding paper.

Suggested Questions

- *If you were given a piece of paper in the shape of the outside rhombus, how would you locate the vertices of the inside rectangle? How about the diamond inside the rectangle?* (Allow students to think about this for a moment. Their answers will vary but will probably focus on locating vertices by measuring to find midpoints of the sides.)

Ask how to accomplish the same goal by folding the paper.

Next, use the Getting Ready questions to focus student attention on midpoints and their coordinates. Students may suggest drawing the line segment from $(0, 8)$ to $(6, 0)$ and examining the right triangle with these two points and $(0, 0)$ as vertices. This gets them the length of the hypotenuse as 10 units, so they know they are trying to divide this into two segments with length 5 units. This suggests looking for scaled-down versions of the right triangle, a strategy that gives accurate estimates for the midpoint of the hypotenuse. This strategy may not be obvious to students for the line segment from $(-2, 1)$ to $(2, -3)$.

Finish the launch by telling students,

- *In this problem, you will explore patterns formed when new polygons are constructed inside of other polygons, especially those that require locating midpoints of given line segments.*

Arrange students in groups of three or four.

Explore 1.3

Circulate as students work on the problem. Ask them how they justify their choices of coordinates in Question A. You may need to prompt students to remember how to calculate distances in a coordinate grid for Question A, part (2) (i.e., remind them to use the Pythagorean Theorem).

Assess whether your students need to discuss Question A before they move through Questions B and C. If so, pull them together to ask,

Suggested Questions

- *How do you find coordinates of the midpoint for a segment joining points (0, 4) and (8, 0)? How about a segment joining (−8, 0) and (0, −4)?*

Questions B and C are extensions of the midpoint idea. You might need to make them the focus of a second day on this problem.

Summarize 1.3

Suggested Questions

- *What coordinates did you come up with for the midpoints of sides on Dalton's quadrilateral?* (Answers should be $(3, 2)$, $(1, -2)$, $(-4, -1)$, and $(-2, 3)$; have students show how to check that these points are midpoints by working through at least one case of checking that distances from endpoints to the midpoint are equal using the Pythagorean theorem.)

- *How about coordinates for the midpoint of the segment joining (x_1, y_1) and (x_2, y_2)?* (There are probably several strategies that the students might come up with:

$$(x_1 + \frac{x_2 - x_1}{2}, y_1 + \frac{y_2 - y_1}{2})$$

is equivalent to the more efficient

$$(\frac{x_2 + x_1}{2}, \frac{y_2 + y_1}{2})$$

This shows that the midpoint of the line segment is located at the midpoint (halfway point) of the two x-values and the midpoint of the two y-values.)

- *What seemed special about the quadrilateral drawn inside of the given polygon?* (It should look like a parallelogram. Use slopes to check that opposite sides are parallel.)

- *Do you think that would happen for some other quadrilaterals? Did you try some other examples to see?* (It should always work.)

Note that we do not ask students to prove that this figure is always a parallelogram. There is an extension problem that outlines this proof. Students needing a challenge and who are interested in this relationship can be asked to find conditions under which the polygon formed by the midpoints of a quadrilateral will be a rhombus, a rectangle, or a square.

1.3 Finding Midpoints

Mathematical Goals

- Find the midpoint of any given line segment
- Explore the special properties of figures determined by connecting midpoints of sides of quadrilaterals

Launch

Draw students' attention to the figure shown in the introduction.

- *If you were given a piece of paper in the shape of the outside rhombus, how would you locate the vertices of the inside rectangle? How about the diamond inside the rectangle?*

- *How can you accomplish the same goal by folding the paper?*

- *In this problem, you will explore patterns formed when new polygons are constructed inside of other polygons, especially those that require locating midpoints of given line segments.*

Arrange students in groups of three or four.

Materials
- Transparencies 1.3 A–C

Vocabulary
- midpoint

Explore

Ask them how they justify their choices of coordinates in Question A. You may need to prompt students to remember how to calculate distances in a coordinate grid for Question A, part (2).

Assess whether your students need to discuss Question A before they move through Questions B and C. Questions B and C are extensions of the midpoint idea. You might need to make them the focus of a second day on this problem.

Summarize

- *How do you find coordinates of the midpoint for a segment joining points such as (0, 4) and (8, 0)? How about the segment joining (-8, 0) and (0, -4)?*

To stimulate sharing of observations on Questions B and C ask:

- *What coordinates did you come up with for the midpoints of sides on Dalton's quadrilateral?*

Have students check that these points are midpoints by working through at least one case of checking that distances from endpoints to the midpoint are equal using the Pythagorean theorem.

- *How about coordinates for the midpoint of the segment joining (x_1, y_1) and (x_2, y_2)?*

- *What seemed special about the quadrilateral drawn inside of the given polygon?*

Materials
- Student notebooks

continued on next page

- *Do you think that would happen for some other quadrilaterals? Did you try some other examples to see?*

ACE Assignment Guide for Problem 1.3

Differentiated Instruction
Solutions for All Learners

Core 17–23, 52–55
Other *Connections* 56–59, *Extensions* 62–65 and unassigned choices from previous problems

Adapted For suggestions about adapting Exercise 17 and other ACE exercises, see the CMP *Special Needs Handbook*.
Connecting to Prior Units 52–54: *Thinking with Mathematical Models*; 55: *Accentuate the Negative*; 56–59: *Say It With Symbols*

Answers to Problem 1.3

A. 1. Midpoint of *AB* is (4, 2); midpoint of *AD* is (−4, 2).

  2. Since the slope of each line *SP* and *DB* is 0, ($\frac{0}{-16}$ and $\frac{0}{-8}$), the two lines are parallel. Therefore the two triangles are similar since all their angles are equal. The scale factor is 2; we can see this by comparing side lengths for *PS* and *BD*. Since the scale factor is 2, we know $AP = \frac{1}{2}AB$, so *P* is a midpoint.

  3. The midpoint of *BC* is (4, −2) and the midpoint of *CD* is (−4, −2).

  4. The distance from either *A* or *B* to the midpoint of $\overline{AB}$ is $\sqrt{20}$. One way to find $\sqrt{20}$ is to draw a vertical line segment from the midpoint (4, 2) to the *x*-axis, which forms a right triangle with legs of length 2 and 4. Use the Pythagorean theorem to find the distance from the midpoint (4, 2) to B: $4^2 + 2^2 = c^2$ where *c* is the distance from B to the midpoint of *AB*. Thus the value for $c = \sqrt{20}$. Similarly, to find the distance from *A* to the midpoint of *AB* a triangle can be formed by drawing a horizontal line segment from the midpoint (4, 2) to the *y*-axis. Since the rhombus has line symmetry about the *x*- and *y*-axes, the distances from

all the midpoints to one of the respective endpoints are also $\sqrt{20}$.

B. 1. Dalton's plan involves drawing a right triangle using the line segment for a hypotenuse and then dividing the horizontal and vertical legs in half. The resulting figure has two congruent right triangles. The original segment is divided into two equal lengths. This procedure would work with any original segment unless the segment is vertical or horizontal.

  2. Vertices are *P* (1, 4), *Q* (5, 0), *R* (−3, −4), and *S* (−5, 2); Midpoints are (3, 2), (1, −2), (−4, −1), and (−2, 3).

  3. a. There are several strategies that the students might come up with. The most likely is to take the average of the *x*-coordinates and take the average of the *y*-coordinates of the endpoints.

  b. Using the strategy in part (a), the midpoint of the line segment with endpoints (*a*, *b*) and (*c*, *d*) has coordinates $\left(\frac{a+c}{2}, \frac{b+d}{2}\right)$.

C. 1. Since slopes of opposite sides are the same, they are parallel, confirming that the inside quadrilateral is a parallelogram. The slopes are 2 and $-\frac{1}{5}$.

  2. Students should produce a variety of different quadrilaterals to check the conjecture that the figure formed by connected midpoints of sides of any quadrilateral will always be a parallelogram. Whether they do it with coordinates or by drawing with a ruler, the result should always be confirmed. A proof using similar triangles is outlined in one of the extension problems.

  3. When midpoints of the sides of a quadrilateral are connected in order, the resulting figure is a *parallelogram*.

Equations for Circles and Polygons

The photo below shows a "crop circle." Not all crop circles are made in crop fields, nor are they all circles. However, the term "crop circles" is often used to describe all such designs. Designs like these have appeared in fields around the world. At first, the origins of the crop circles were unknown. However, in many cases, the people who made them have come forward and taken credit for their work.

Getting Ready for Problem 1.1

Suppose you are planning to make a crop circle design like the one above.

- How can you outline the circle accurately?
- How can you locate sides and vertices of the other shapes in the design?
- How can you use equations and coordinate graphs to help plan your design?

Notes _____

_____

_____

_____

Equations for Circles

Y
ou can outline the outer circle of a crop circle by using a rope. Anchor one end of the rope where you want the center of the circle. Hold the other end and, with the rope pulled taut, walk around the center point.

To plan the other parts of the design, it helps to draw the circle on a coordinate grid. In this problem, you will find an equation relating the coordinates of the points on a circle.

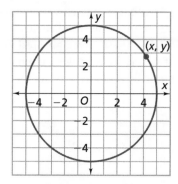

On the circle above, are there points for which it is easy to find the coordinates?

What mathematical ideas can help you find coordinates of other points on the circle?

Problem 1.1 Equations for Circles

A. 1. The circle above has a radius of 5 units and is centered at the origin. Estimate the missing coordinate for these points on the circle. If there is more than one possible point, give the missing coordinate for each possibility.

 a. $(0, \blacksquare)$ **b.** $(\blacksquare, 0)$ **c.** $(3, \blacksquare)$

 d. $(4, \blacksquare)$ **e.** $(\blacksquare, -3)$ **f.** $(\blacksquare, 4)$

 g. $(-2, \blacksquare)$ **h.** $(\blacksquare, 2)$ **i.** $(\blacksquare, 5)$

 2. Which of your coordinates from part (1) do you think are exactly correct? How do you know?

Notes _____

_____

_____

_____

B. Think about a point (x, y) starting at $(5, 0)$ and moving counterclockwise, tracing around the circle.

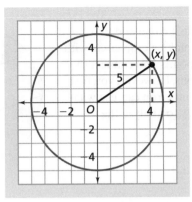

1. How does the y-coordinate of the point change as the x-coordinate approaches zero and then becomes negative?

2. The radius from the origin $(0, 0)$ to the point (x, y) has a length of 5 units. The diagram shows that you can make two right triangles with the radius as the hypotenuse. How do these triangles change as the point moves around the circle?

3. Use what you know about the relationship among the side lengths of a right triangle to write an equation relating x and y to the radius, 5.

4. Kaitlyn says that the relationship is $x + y = 5$ or $y = 5 - x$. Is she correct? Explain.

5. Does every point on the circle satisfy your equation? Explain.

C. These points are all on the circle. Check that they satisfy the equation you wrote in Question B part (3).

1. $(3, 4)$ 2. $(-4, 3)$ 3. $(\sqrt{13}, \sqrt{12})$ 4. $(0, -5)$

5. Does any point *not* on the circle satisfy the equation? Explain.

D. 1. Give the coordinates of three points in the interior of the circle. What can you say about the x- and y-coordinates of points inside the circle?

2. Use your equation from Question B to help you write an *inequality* that describes the points in the interior of the circle.

E. How can you change your equation from Question B to represent a circle with a radius of 1, 3, or 10 units?

ACE Homework starts on page 12.

Notes _____

_____

_____

_____

1.2 Parallels and Perpendiculars

The design at the right is made from a circle and two overlapping rectangles. One way to make a crop circle with this design is to place stakes at key points and connect the stakes with string outlining the regions. However, you first need to find the location of these points. You can use what you know about coordinate geometry to analyze the design's key points and features.

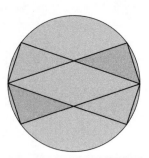

Problem 1.2 Parallels and Perpendiculars

This diagram shows some of the key points in the design. The design has reflection symmetry in both the *x*-axis and the *y*-axis. The radius is 5 units.

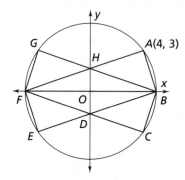

A. Find the coordinates of points *B*, *C*, *E*, *F*, and *G*.

B. List all pairs of parallel lines. How do the slopes of the lines in each pair compare? Explain why this makes sense.

C. List all pairs of perpendicular lines. How do the slopes of the lines in each pair compare? Explain why this makes sense.

D. Locate a new point *K*(2, *y*) on the circle. Draw a line segment from point *K* to the point (5, 0). Can you draw a rectangle with this segment as one side and all its vertices on the circle? If so, give the coordinates of the vertices.

8   The Shapes of Algebra

Notes _____

_____

_____

_____

E. 1. Kara was sketching on grid paper to try out some design ideas. She got interrupted! On a copy of Kara's diagram below, complete the polygons specified. (There may be more than one way to draw each one.) The polygons should all fit on the grid and should not overlap.

- Rectangle *ABCD*
- Parallelogram *EFGH*
- Parallelogram *PQRS*
- Rectangle *TUVW*

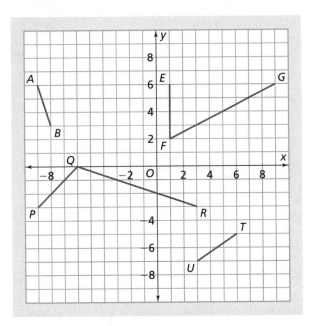

2. Give the coordinates of the vertex points for each figure.

3. Compare the slopes for all pairs of parallel sides. Describe the patterns you see. Are the patterns the same as you found in Question B?

4. Compare the slopes for all pairs of perpendicular sides. Describe the patterns you see. Are the patterns the same as you found in Question C?

5. What is true about the equations for a pair of parallel lines? What is true about the equations for a pair of perpendicular lines?

ACE Homework starts on page 12.

Investigation 1 Equations for Circles and Polygons   **9**

Notes _____

_____

_____

_____

Finding Midpoints

Dalton's class wants to design some interesting crop circles that are not circles. He starts with a diamond design.

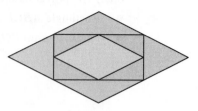

To draw this diamond design, you start with the outer rhombus. You connect the midpoints of its sides to form a rectangle, and then connect the midpoints of the rectangle's sides.

What would you need to check to know that the yellow shape is a rectangle?

How could you create this pattern by measuring and drawing or by folding paper and tracing creases?

Getting Ready for Problem

To make symmetric designs on a coordinate grid, it is helpful to have strategies for finding the coordinates of midpoints of line segments.

- How can you find the length of the line segment from $(0, 8)$ to $(6, 0)$ and from $(-2, 1)$ to $(2, -3)$?

- How can you estimate the coordinates of the midpoint of each segment?

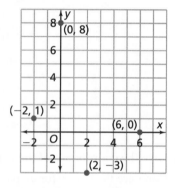

Problem Finding Midpoints

A. The figure at the right is a rhombus.

1. Estimate coordinates of P, the midpoint of side AB. Estimate the coordinates of S, the midpoint of side AD.

2. Explain why $\triangle APS$ is similar to $\triangle ABD$. What is the scale factor? How can you use these facts to check the coordinates of P and S? How can you use these facts to confirm that P and S are the midpoints?

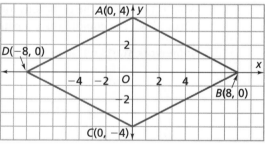

10 The Shapes of Algebra

Notes _____

_____

_____

_____

3. Find the midpoints of sides *BC* and *CD*.

4. Check the midpoint coordinates by calculating the distance from each midpoint to the endpoints of the segments on which it is located. (Hint: Use symmetry to limit the calculations you do.)

B. Dalton tries a quadrilateral that is not symmetric.

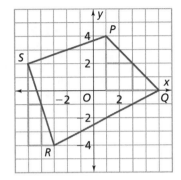

1. Dalton draws some lines on the quadrilateral to help him locate the midpoints of *PQ* and *SR*. Does this seem like a plan that would work no matter where *P* and *Q* or *S* and *R* are located? Explain.

2. Find coordinates of the midpoint of each side.

3. a. For each side, compare the coordinates of the endpoints to the coordinates of the midpoint. See if you can find a strategy for finding the coordinates of the midpoint of any line segment.

b. Use your findings to complete this statement:

The midpoint of the segment with endpoints (a, b) and (c, d) has coordinates . . .

C. Dalton connected the midpoints of the sides of *PQRS* to form a quadrilateral.

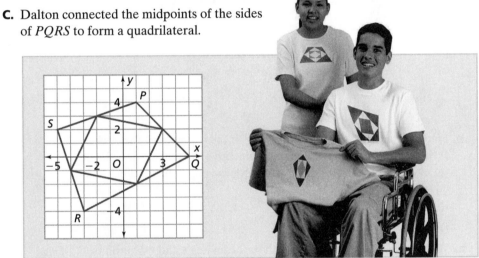

1. The quadrilateral appears to be a parallelogram. Verify this by finding the slopes of its sides.

2. Draw several quadrilaterals of your own. For each quadrilateral, find the midpoints of the sides (by measuring or paper folding), and connect those midpoints in order.

3. Describe the pattern in your results by completing this sentence:

When the midpoints of the sides of a quadrilateral are connected in order, the resulting figure is . . .

ACE Homework starts on page 12.

Investigation 1 Equations for Circles and Polygons **11**

Notes _____

_____

_____

_____

Applications

1. a. Write an equation that relates the coordinates x and y for points on the circle.

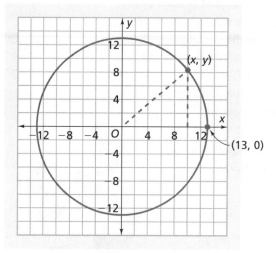

b. Find the missing coordinates for each of these points on the circle. If there is more than one possible point, give the missing coordinate for each possibility. Show that each ordered pair satisfies the equation.

$(0, ■)$ $(5, ■)$ $(-4, ■)$ $(-8, ■)$

$(■, 10)$ $(■, -6)$ $(■, 0)$ $(■, -2)$

c. Write an inequality that relates the coordinates x and y for points inside the circle.

d. Choose any point in the interior of the circle and confirm that this point is a solution for the inequality you wrote in part (c).

e. Choose any point outside the circle and check that it is not a solution for the inequality you wrote in part (c).

12   The Shapes of Algebra

Notes _____

_____

_____

_____

2. a. Write an equation that relates the coordinates x and y for points on the circle.

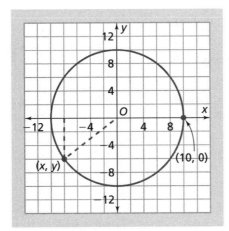

b. Find the missing coordinates for each of these points on the circle. If there is more than one possible point, give the missing coordinate for each possibility. Show that each ordered pair satisfies the equation.

$(8, \blacksquare)$ $(3, \blacksquare)$ $(-4, \blacksquare)$ $(0, \blacksquare)$

$(\blacksquare, -4)$ $(\blacksquare, -6)$ $(\blacksquare, 0)$ $(\blacksquare, 2)$

c. Write an inequality that describes the points in the interior of the circle.

d. Write an inequality that describes the points outside the circle.

e. Choose one point in the interior of the circle and one point outside the circle and confirm these are solutions for the appropriate inequalities.

active math
online
For: Algebra Tools
Visit: PHSchool.com
Web Code: apd-7102

Investigation 1 Equations for Circles and Polygons   **13**

Notes _____

_____

_____

_____

3. On a copy of this diagram, draw quadrilaterals meeting the conditions in parts (a)–(d). Your figures should fit entirely on the grid and should not overlap.

Homework Help Online
PHSchool.com

For: Help with Exercise 3
Web Code: ape-7103

    a. Rectangle *ABCD* lies entirely in the second quadrant.

    b. Rectangle *EFGH* lies entirely in the first quadrant.

    c. Rectangle *PQRS* is not a square. It lies entirely in the third quadrant except for vertex *Q*.

    d. Square *TUVW* lies entirely in the fourth quadrant.

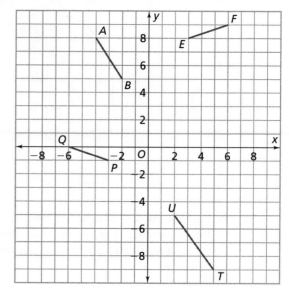

4. The quadrilaterals named in parts (a)–(d) are parallelograms formed on the diagram at the right. Give the coordinates for the fourth vertex. Then, calculate the slopes of the sides to show that the opposite sides are parallel.

    a. *JKLM*

    b. *NPQR*

    c. *STUV*

    d. *WYXZ*

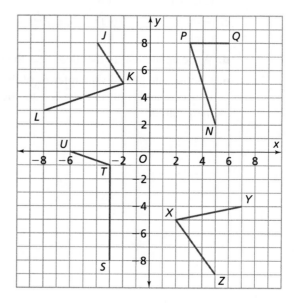

STUDENT PAGE

Notes _____

_____

_____

_____

Find the equation of a line parallel to the given line.

5. $y = 2x + 3$ **6.** $y = -4x + 7$

7. $y = -3x + 5$ **8.** $y = \frac{1}{2}x - 12$

9. $y = -\frac{2}{3}x - 4$ **10.** $y = 6x - 9$

For Exercises 11–16, find the equation of a line perpendicular to the given line.

11. $y = 3x + 2$ **12.** $y = -\frac{3}{4}x - 2$

13. $y = -2x + 7$ **14.** $y = 5x - 1$

15. $y = \frac{1}{2}x + 3$ **16.** $y = -4x - 5$

17. a. The circle in this design is centered at the origin. Find coordinates for points *J*, *K*, and *L*.

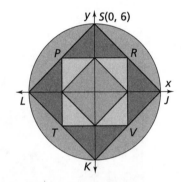

b. Points *P*, *R*, *V*, and *T* are the midpoints of the segments on which they lie. Find coordinates for each of these points.

c. Find coordinates of the vertices of the innermost quadrilateral. Is this quadrilateral a square? Explain.

Find the midpoint of the segment with the given endpoints.

18. $(0, 0)$ and $(4, 6)$ **19.** $(3, 2)$ and $(7, -4)$

20. $(1, 2)$ and $(8, 5)$ **21.** $(1, 2)$ and $(-5, 6)$

22. $(0, 0)$ and $(-4, -7)$ **23.** $(-1, -5)$ and $(-6, 2)$

Notes _____

_____

_____

_____

Connections

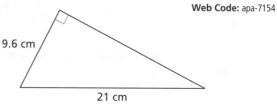

Use the Pythagorean Theorem to find the unknown side length.

For: Multiple-Choice Skills Practice
Web Code: apa-7154

24.

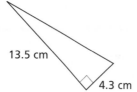

8 cm

12.2 cm

25.

9.6 cm

21 cm

26.

13.5 cm

4.3 cm

27.

11 cm

9.2 cm

Write an equation for the line with the given slope and y-intercept.

28. slope $\frac{1}{2}$, y-intercept $(0, 3)$

29. slope $-\frac{1}{3}$, y-intercept $(0, 5)$

30. slope 6, y-intercept $(0, \frac{1}{2})$

Write an equation for the line with the given slope and that passes through the given point.

31. slope 2, point $(3, 1)$

32. slope -4, point $(-1, 7)$

33. slope $-\frac{5}{6}$, point $(0, 5)$

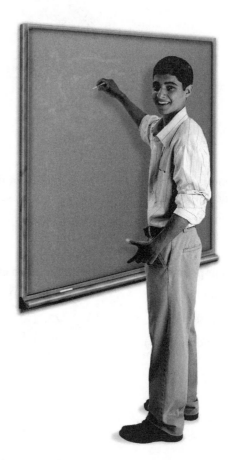

Notes _____

_____

_____

_____

34. For each type of quadrilateral in the first column, identify all the properties from the second column that apply to that type of quadrilateral.

Quadrilateral Types	Properties
a. square	**i.** Two pairs of parallel sides
b. rectangle	**ii.** Four right angles
c. rhombus	**iii.** Two pairs of congruent sides
d. parallelogram	**iv.** Interior angle measures with a sum of 360°
	v. Opposite angle measures with a sum of 180°
	vi. Perpendicular diagonals

For Exercises 35–46, find the value of each expression.

35. $12 + (-18)$ **36.** $-9 + (-19)$ **37.** $-32 - 73$

38. $-23 - (-12)$ **39.** $90 - (-24)$ **40.** $34 - 76$

41. $-22 \times (-3)$ **42.** $5 \times (-13)$ **43.** -12×20

44. $-24 \div 6$ **45.** $-42 \div (-2)$ **46.** $84 \div (-4)$

47. Suppose you've drawn a design on a coordinate grid. Tell whether each coordinate rule will produce a similar design.

  a. $(x, y) \rightarrow (x + 2, y + 3)$ **b.** $(x, y) \rightarrow (2x, 3y)$

  c. $(x, y) \rightarrow (2.5x, 2.5y)$ **d.** $(x, y) \rightarrow (-2x, -2y)$

48. The radius of this crop design is 6 meters.

  a. What is the area of the smaller square?

  b. What is the area of the region between the smaller and larger squares?

  c. What is the area of the region between the larger square and the circle?

  d. Describe all the symmetries in the design.

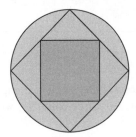

49. a. Consider the points $A(-2, 2)$, $B(-1, -1)$, $C(-1, 2)$, $D(0, -3)$, $E(0, 2)$, $F(1, 0)$, $G(2, 0)$, $H(4, -1)$, $J(5, -1)$, $K(6, -1.5)$. Without plotting points or drawing lines, find the slope of these lines.

    line AB line CD line EF line GH line JK

  b. Order the slopes in part (a) from least to greatest.

Notes _____

_____

_____

_____

50. a. Suppose you connect the midpoints of the sides of a triangle as shown below to form a smaller triangle. How does the perimeter of the blue triangle compare to that of the original triangle?

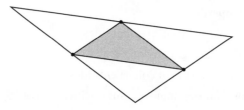

b. How does the area of the blue triangle compare to that of the original triangle?

51. Two students became intrigued by crop designs. They did a project comparing the occurrences of different shapes in three countries, A, B and C.

CROP CIRCLE OCCURRENCES

Boundary Type	Country A	Country B	Country C
Circle	12	12	6
Square	8	3	9

a. Make a circle graph to compare the total number of circular crop designs in three countries with the total number of square crop designs.

b. Make a bar graph to compare the crop designs from countries A, B, and C.

c. Make three statements summarizing the students' findings on crop designs in the three countries.

Find the equation of the line through the points.

52. $(2, 3)$ and $(0, 1)$

53. $(-1, 3)$ and $(2, -9)$

54. $(-1, -1)$ and $(3, 7)$

18 The Shapes of Algebra

Notes _____

_____

_____

_____

55. Kara started to find the midpoints of some segments, but she didn't finish. Her work is shown in parts (a)–(c). Finish her calculations to find the midpoint. Then give the coordinates of the segment's endpoints.

a. $\left(\dfrac{-3 + 9}{2}, \dfrac{-1 + 1}{2}\right)$

b. $\left(\dfrac{-3 - 4}{2}, \dfrac{-7 + 1}{2}\right)$

c. $\left(\dfrac{-3 + (-9)}{2}, \dfrac{-1 + (-1)}{2}\right)$

For Exercises 56–58, tell whether the lines intersect. If they do, find their intersection point both algebraically *and* graphically. If they don't intersect, explain how you know.

56. $y = x - 11$ and $y = 3x + 23$

57. $y = 2x + 10$ and $y = x + 20$

58. $y = 3x + 9$ and $y = 3(x + 10)$

59. Multiple Choice Which expression is equivalent to $3x + 10$?

   A. $3(x + 10)$ **B.** $3x + 7x$

   C. $5(x + 2) - 2x$ **D.** $2x - 5x + 10$

Extensions

60. This circle has radius 5 and center $(1, 2)$. Find or estimate the missing coordinates for these points on the circle. In each case, use the Pythagorean Theorem to check that the point is 5 units from the center.

a. $(\blacksquare, 6)$

b. $(5, \blacksquare)$

c. $(-3, \blacksquare)$

d. $(1, \blacksquare)$

e. $(\blacksquare, 2)$

f. $(4, \blacksquare)$

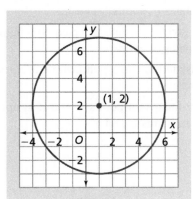

Notes _____

_____

_____

_____

61. a. This circle has radius 5 and center (1, 2). $\overline{AC}$ is parallel to the x-axis. $\overline{BC}$ is parallel to the y-axis. What are the lengths of $\overline{AC}$, $\overline{BC}$, $\overline{AB}$ in terms of x and y?

b. What equation shows how these side lengths are related?

c. Suppose you redraw the figure with $B(x, y)$ in a different position, but still on the circle. Would the coordinates of B still fit the equation you wrote in part (b)?

d. Based on this example, what do you think is the general equation for points on a circle with center (m, n) and radius r?

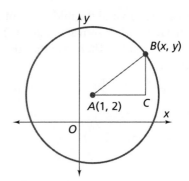

62. a. The vertices of the blue triangle are the midpoints of the sides of $\triangle FGH$. How are the sides of the blue triangle related to those of $\triangle FGH$? Use coordinates to check your ideas.

b. Draw several more triangles and connect their midpoints to form a smaller triangle. Record your observations.

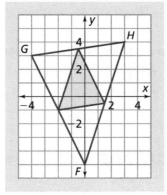

63. Consider the points $O(0, 0)$, $X(4, 5)$, $L(2, 3)$, and $M(6, 8)$.

a. Points U and V divide $\overline{OX}$ into three equal-length segments. Find the coordinates of points U and V.

b. Points W and Z divide $\overline{LM}$ into three equal-length segments. Find the coordinates of points W and Z.

c. $\overline{OX}$ can be translated to correspond with $\overline{LM}$. Describe the rule for this translation.

d. Check your coordinates for points W and Z by applying your translation rule to points U and V.

20   The Shapes of Algebra

Notes _____

_____

_____

_____

64. Use the diagram below. Record your answers to parts (a)–(c) in a copy of the table at the bottom of the page.

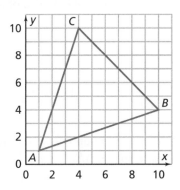

a. Find the coordinates of points X and Y that divide $\overline{AC}$ into three equal-length segments.

b. Find the coordinates of points M and N that divide $\overline{BC}$ into three equal-length segments.

c. Find the coordinates of points P and Q that divide $\overline{AB}$ into three equal-length segments.

d. Describe the pattern relating the coordinates of the endpoints to the coordinates of the two points that divide the segment into thirds.

e. How can you find the coordinates of the two points R and S that divide the segment joining points $G(x_1, y_1)$ and $H(x_2, y_2)$ into three equal-length segments?

Segment	Endpoint	Dividing Point	Dividing Point	Endpoint
$\overline{AC}$	$A(\blacksquare, \blacksquare)$	$X(\blacksquare, \blacksquare)$	$Y(\blacksquare, \blacksquare)$	$C(\blacksquare, \blacksquare)$
$\overline{BC}$	$B(\blacksquare, \blacksquare)$	$M(\blacksquare, \blacksquare)$	$N(\blacksquare, \blacksquare)$	$C(\blacksquare, \blacksquare)$
$\overline{AB}$	$A(\blacksquare, \blacksquare)$	$P(\blacksquare, \blacksquare)$	$Q(\blacksquare, \blacksquare)$	$B(\blacksquare, \blacksquare)$

Notes _____

_____

_____

_____

65. Multiple Choice In triangle ABC, point D is on $\overline{AB}$ and point E is on $\overline{AC}$, such that $2AD = DB$ and $2AE = EC$. $2AD$ means twice the length of AD and $2AE$ means twice the length of AE. Which of the following statements is *not* true?

A. $\triangle ADE$ is similar to $\triangle ABC$

B. $BC = 3DE$

C. $\overline{DE}$ is parallel to $\overline{BC}$

D. area of $\triangle ABC = 3$(area of $\triangle ADE$)

66. In this diagram, the vertices of $PQRS$ are the midpoints of the sides of quadrilateral $WXYZ$. $\overline{WY}$ is twice as long as $\overline{SR}$.

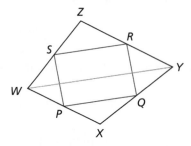

a. Explain why $\triangle WZY$ is similar to $\triangle SZR$.

b. How does the similarity of $\triangle WZY$ and $\triangle SZR$ imply that $\overline{SR}$ is parallel to $\overline{WY}$?

c. How could you show that $\overline{PQ}$ is parallel to $\overline{WY}$?

d. Why do the results of parts (b) and (c) imply that $\overline{SR}$ is parallel to $\overline{PQ}$?

e. How could you repeat the reasoning from parts (a)–(d) to show that $\overline{SP}$ is parallel to $\overline{RQ}$?

f. How does the reasoning from parts (a)–(e) show that $PQRS$ is a parallelogram?

Notes _____

_____

_____

_____

Mathematical Reflections 1

The problems of this investigation challenged you to find patterns in the coordinates of points on line segments and circles. These questions will help you summarize what you have learned.

Think about your answers to these questions. Discuss your ideas with other students and your teacher. Then write a summary of your findings in your notebook.

Give specific examples to illustrate your answers to Questions 1–3.

1. What types of equations or inequalities describe points (x, y) that lie

   a. on a circle of radius r centered at the origin?

   b. in the interior of a circle of radius r centered at the origin?

2. The equations $y = mx + b$ and $y = nx + c$ represent two lines. How can you tell whether the lines are

   a. parallel?

   b. perpendicular?

3. How can you find the midpoint of the segment with endpoints (a, b) and (c, d)?

Notes _____

_____

_____

_____

Answers Applications Connections Extensions

Investigation

ACE Assignment Choices

Differentiated Instruction Solutions for All Learners

Problem 1.1
Core 1–2, 24–27, 31–33, 35–46
Other 28–30, 34, 60, 61, and unassigned choices from previous problems

Problem 1.2
Core 4–16, 49
Other 3, 47, 48, 50, 51 and unassigned choices from previous problems

Problem 1.3
Core 17–23, 52–55
Other 56–59, 62–66 and unassigned choices from previous problems

Adapted For suggestions about adapting Exercise 17 and other ACE exercises, see the CMP *Special Needs Handbook*.
Connecting to Prior Units 24–27: *Looking for Pythagoras*; 28–33, 49: *Moving Straight Ahead*; 35–46, 55: *Accentuate the Negative*; 34: *Kaleidoscopes, Hubcaps, and Mirrors*; 47: *Stretching and Shrinking*; 48: *Covering and Surrounding*; 48: *Kaleidoscopes, Hubcaps, and Mirrors*; 50: *Stretching and Shrinking*; 51: *Data Distribution*; 52–54: *Thinking with Mathematical Models*; 56–59: *Say it With Symbols*

Applications

1. **a.** $x^2 + y^2 = 169$

   b. $(0, 13)$ and $(0, -13)$; check to see points satisfy equation: $0^2 + 13^2 = 169$ and $0^2 + (-13)^2 = 169$.

   $(5, 12)$ and $(5, -12)$; check to see points satisfy equation: $5^2 + 12^2 = 169$ and $5^2 + (-12)^2 = 169$.

   $(-4, 12.4)$ and $(-4, -12.4)$ are approximations. The exact values of the y-coordinates can be found by solving the equation $(-4)^2 + y^2 = 169$ for $y = \pm\sqrt{153}$.

   $(-8, 10.2)$ and $(-8, -10.2)$ are approximations. The exact values of the y-coordinates can be found by solving the equation $(-8)^2 + y^2 = 169$ for $y = \pm\sqrt{105}$.

   $(8.3, 10)$ and $(-8.3, 10)$ are approximations. The exact values of the x-coordinates can be found by solving the equation $x^2 + 10^2 = 169$ for $x = \pm\sqrt{69}$.

   $(11.5, -6)$ and $(-11.5, -6)$ are approximations. The exact values of the x-coordinates can be found by solving the equation $x^2 + (-6)^2 = 169$ for $x = \pm\sqrt{133}$.

   $(13, 0)$ and $(-13, 0)$; check to see points satisfy equation: $13^2 + 0^2 = 169$ and $(-13)^2 + 0^2 = 169$.

   $(12.8, -2)$ and $(-12.8, -2)$ are approximations. The exact values of the x-coordinates can be found by solving the equation $x^2 + (-2)^2 = 169$ for $x = \pm\sqrt{165}$.

   c. $x^2 + y^2 < 169$

   d. Ex: $(3, 10)$ is inside the circle and accordingly $3^2 + 10^2 = 109 < 169$

   e. Ex: $(10, 11)$ is outside the circle and accordingly $10^2 + 11^2 = 221 > 169$

2. **a.** $x^2 + y^2 = 100$

   b. $(8, 6)$ and $(8, -6)$; check to see points satisfy equation: $8^2 + 6^2 = 100$ and $8^2 + (-6)^2 = 100$.

   $(3, 9.5)$ and $(3, -9.5)$ are approximations. The exact values of the y-coordinates can be found by solving the equation $3^2 + y^2 = 100$ for $y = \pm\sqrt{91}$.

$(-4, 9.2)$ and $(-4, -9.2)$ are approximations. The exact values of the y-coordinates can be found by solving the equation $(-4)^2 + x^2 = 100$ for $y = \pm\sqrt{84}$.

$(0, 10)$ and $(0, -10)$; check to see points satisfy equation: $0^2 + 10^2 = 100$ and $0^2 + (-10)^2 = 100$.

$(9.2, -4)$ and $(-9.2, -4)$ are approximations. The exact values of the x-coordinates can be found by solving the equation $x^2 + (-4)^2 = 100$ for $x = \pm\sqrt{84}$.

$(8, -6)$ and $(-8, -6)$; check to see points satisfy equation: $8^2 + (-6)^2 = 100$ and $(-8)^2 + (-6)^2 = 100$.

$(10, 0)$ and $(-10, 0)$; check to see points satisfy equation: $10^2 + 0^2 = 100$ and $(-10)^2 + 0^2 = 100$.

$(9.8, 2)$ and $(-9.8, 2)$ are approximations. The exact values of the x-coordinates can be found by solving the equation $x^2 + (2)^2 = 100$ for $x = \pm\sqrt{96}$.

c. $x^2 + y^2 < 100$

d. $x^2 + y^2 > 100$

e. Ex: $(5, 4)$ is inside and $(7, 8)$ is outside and accordingly $5^2 + 4^2 = 41 < 100$ and $7^2 + 8^2 = 113 > 100$

3. a. Possibilities with integer coordinates: $C(-5, 3)$ and $D(-7, 6)$ or $C(-8, 1)$ and $D(-10, 4)$

b. Possibilities with integer coordinates: $G(7, 6)$ and $H(4, 5)$ or $G(8, 3)$ and $H(5, 2)$

c. Two possibilities with integer coordinates: $R(-8, -6)$ and $S(-5, -7)$ or $R(-9, -9)$ and $S(-6, -10)$

d. $V(6, -2)$ and $W(9, -6)$

4. a. $M(-10, 6)$; slopes of JK and LM are both $-\frac{3}{2}$; slopes of JM and KL are both $\frac{1}{3}$.

b. $R(8, 2)$; slopes of NP and RQ are -3; slopes of PQ and NR are 0.

c. $V(6, -7)$; slopes of TU and SV are $-\frac{1}{4}$; slopes of UV and ST are undefined.

d. $W(10, -8)$; slopes of YZ and XW are $-\frac{4}{3}$; slopes of WZ and XY are $\frac{1}{5}$.

5. Answers will vary. The slope must be 2 but the y-intercept will change.

6. Answers will vary. The slope must be -4, but the y-intercept will change.

7. Answers will vary. The slope must be -3, but the y-intercept will change.

8. Answers will vary. The slope must be $\frac{1}{2}$, but the y-intercept will change.

9. Answers will vary. The slope must be $-\frac{2}{3}$, but the y-intercept will change.

10. Answers will vary. The slope must be 6, but the y-intercept will change.

11. Answers will vary. The slope of the new line must be the negative reciprocal of the slope of the original line $(-\frac{1}{3})$, but the y-intercept can change.

12. Answers will vary. The slope of the new line must be $\frac{4}{3}$, but the y-intercept can change.

13. Answers will vary. The slope of the new line must be $\frac{1}{2}$, but the y-intercept can change.

14. Answers will vary. The slope of the new line must be $-\frac{1}{5}$, but the y-intercept can change.

15. Answers will vary. The slope of the new line must be -2, but the y-intercept can change.

16. Answers will vary. The slope of the new line must be $\frac{1}{4}$, but the y-intercept can change.

17. a. $J(6, 0)$, $K(0, -6)$, $L(-6, 0)$

b. $P(-3, 3)$, $R(3, 3)$, $V(3, -3)$, $T(-3, -3)$

c. Innermost square vertex coordinates are $(3, 0)$, $(0, -3)$, $(-3, 0)$, and $(0, 3)$. Yes, this is a square because the distance between points is the same.

18. $(2, 3)$ **19.** $(5, -1)$ **20.** $(4.5, 3.5)$

21. $(-2, 4)$ **22.** $(-2, -3.5)$ **23.** $(-3.5, -1.5)$

Connections

24. $\sqrt{212.84} \approx 14.6$ cm

25. $\sqrt{348.84} \approx 18.7$ cm

26. $\sqrt{200.74} \approx 14.2$ cm

27. $\sqrt{36.36} \approx 6$ cm   **28.** $y = \frac{1}{2}x + 3$

29. $y = -\frac{1}{3}x + 5$ **30.** $y = 6x + \frac{1}{2}$

31. $y = 2x - 5$ **32.** $y = -4x + 3$

33. $y = -\frac{5}{6}x + 5$

34. a. Squares have all the listed properties (i–vi).

   b. Rectangles have all the properties but perpendicular diagonals (vi).

   c. i, iii, iv, vi   **d.** i, iii, iv

35. -6 **36.** -28 **37.** -105 **38.** -11

39. 114   **40.** -42 **41.** 66   **42.** -65

43. -240 **44.** -4 **45.** 21   **46.** -21

47. a, c, and d will produce a similar copy

48. a. 36 m^2 **b.** 36 m^2

   c. $(36\pi - 72)$ m^2 or approximately 41 m^2

   d. The figure has all the symmetries of a square: vertical, horizontal, and two diagonal lines. It also has rotation symmetry of 90° and all multiples of 90°.

49. a. Slope of $AB = -3$

   Slope of $CD = -5$

   Slope of $EF = -2$

   Slope of $GH = \frac{-1}{2}$

   Slope of $JK = -0.5$

   b. Ordering slopes from least to greatest: $\frac{-1}{2} = -0.5, -2, -3, -5$.

50. a. We can show that each of the unshaded triangles are similar to the large triangle with scale factor 2. So, perimeter of smaller shaded triangle is one-half that of the larger, since each side of the small triangle is one-half as long as the corresponding side of the largest triangle.

   b. Area of the small triangle is one-fourth that of the larger, since base and height of the shaded smaller triangle are each one-half the corresponding dimensions of those in the larger triangle.

51. a. The circle graph should show 60% circle boundaries and 40% square boundaries as shown below:

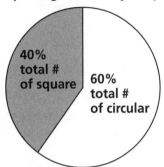

Crop Design Boundary Shapes

40% total # of square   60% total # of circular

   b. There should be 6 bars, two for country A, two for country B, and two for country C to represent the circular boundaries and square boundaries. If the students place the bars side by side, comparisons are easier. An example of a bar graph is shown below.

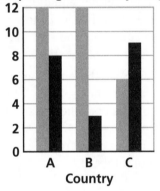

Crop Design Boundary Shapes

Country

■ square boundary

   c. Possible statements: countries A and B had the same number of crop designs with a circular boundary which can be seen in the bar graph since these bars are the same height. In total, there are only 50% more circular boundaries than square crop design boundaries in the three countries. The total number of crop designs for country A is 20, country B is 15, and country C is 15. This can be seen on the bar graph by adding the two bars' heights (circle and square) for each country.

52. $y = x + 1$

53. $y = -4x - 1$

54. $y = 2x + 1$

55. a. Midpoint: $(3, 0)$

Endpoints: $(-3, -1)$ and $(9, 1)$ or $(-3, 1)$ and $(9, -1)$

b. Midpoint: $(-3.5, -3)$

Endpoints: $(-3, -7)$ and $(-4, 1)$ or $(-3, 1)$ and $(-4, -7)$

c. Midpoint: $(-6, -1)$

Endpoints: $(-3, -1), (-9, -1)$

56. Intersect; the point of intersection is $(-17, -28)$, which can be found by solving the equation $x - 11 = 3x + 23$ for x and then substituting this value into either equation $y = x - 11$ or $y = 3x + 23$ to find y. To solve graphically, graph the equations and find the coordinates of their point of intersection.

57. Intersect; the point of intersection is $(10, 30)$, which can be found by solving the equation $2x + 10 = x + 20$ for x and then substituting this value into either equation $y = 2x + 10$ or $y = x + 20$ to find y. To solve graphically, graph the equations and find the coordinates of their point of intersection.

58. Do not intersect; these lines are parallel lines since the equation $y = 3x + 9$ has an m value of 3 as does the equation $y = 3(x + 10) = 3x + 30$. The lines are parallel and have different y-intercepts; thus they do not intersect.

59. C

Extensions

60. a. $(-2, 6)$ and $(4, 6)$ [Check: $(-2 - 1)^2 + (6-2)^2 = (-3)^2 + 4^2 = 9 + 16 = 25$; $(4-1)^2 + (6-2)^2 = 3^2 + 4^2 = 9 + 16 = 25$]

b. $(5, 5)$ [Check: $4^2 + 3^2 = 5^2$] and $(5, -1)$ [Check: $4^2 + (-3)^2 = 5^2$]

c. $(-3, 5)$ and $(-3, -1)$

d. $(1, 7)$ and $(1, -3)$

e. $(6, 2)$ and $(-4, 2)$

f. $(4, 6)$ and $(4, -2)$

61. a. Lengths of $\overline{AC}, \overline{BC},$ and $\overline{AB}$ are $(x - 1)$, $(y - 2)$, and 5, respectively.

b. Equation $(x - 1)^2 + (y - 2)^2 = 5^2$

c. If students choose B as a point in another quadrant (not Quadrant I) they will meet the problem of how to calculate or name the length of each side of the triangle. They may reason from a specific example, say $(-2, 6)$. Then the horizontal distance on the triangle is not "$x - 1$" but "$1 - x$" or "$|x - 1|$." However, the equation involves "$(x - 1)^2$" and so students should notice that, for example, $(-2 - 1)^2 = (1 - (-2))^2$. So, yes, the equation is satisfied by points in other quadrants.

d. Equation $(x - m)^2 + (y - n)^2 = r^2$

62. a. Sides of the inside triangle are parallel to and one-half the length of the corresponding sides of the outer triangle.

b. Results from other test drawings should be the same.

63. a. $U = \left(\frac{4}{3}, \frac{5}{3}\right)$ and $V = \left(\frac{8}{3}, \frac{10}{3}\right)$; subtract the x-coordinate of O from the x-coordinate of X to get the horizontal change of 4 and divide this 3 to get the x-coordinate of U of $\frac{4}{3}$. Subtract the y-coordinate of O from the y-coordinate of X to get the vertical change of 5 and divide this by 3 to get the y-coordinate of U of $\frac{5}{3}$. Add $\frac{4}{3}$ to the x-coordinate of U to get the x-coordinate of V and add $\frac{5}{3}$ to the y-coordinate of U to get the y-coordinate of V.

b. $W = \left(\frac{10}{3}, \frac{14}{3}\right)$ and $Z = \left(\frac{14}{3}, \frac{19}{3}\right)$; Subtract the x-coordinate of L from the x-coordinate of M to the the horizontal change of 4, divide this by 3 and then add it to the x-coordinate of L (since it is not at the origin like in Question A) to get the x-coordinate of W of $2 + \frac{4}{3} = \frac{10}{3}$. Subtract the y-coordinate of L from the y-coordinate of M to get the vertical change of 5, divide this by 3 and then add it to the y-coordinate of L to get the y-coordinate of W of $3 + \frac{5}{3} = \frac{14}{3}$. Add $\frac{4}{3}$ to the x-coordinate of W to get the x-coordinate of Z and add $\frac{5}{3}$ to the y-coordinate of W to get the y-coordinate of Z.

c. The rule for the translation from $\overline{OX}$ to $\overline{LM}$ is add 2 to the x-coordinate and 3 to the y-coordinate or $(x, y) \rightarrow (x + 2, y + 3)$.

d. This translation rule could have been used to check the coordinates of W and Z since $W = (\frac{4}{3} + 2, \frac{5}{3} + 3) = (\frac{10}{3}, \frac{14}{3})$ and $Z = (\frac{8}{3} + 2, \frac{10}{3} + 3) = (\frac{14}{3}, \frac{19}{3})$.

64. (Figure 1)

a. Divide $\overline{AC}$ into thirds by $X = (2, 4)$ and $Y = (3, 7)$.

b. Divide $\overline{BC}$ into thirds by $M = (8, 6)$ and $N = (6, 8)$.

c. Divide $\overline{AB}$ into thirds by $P = (4, 2)$ and $Q = (7, 3)$.

d. If you subtract the x-coordinates (or y-coordinates) for the endpoints and divide by 3, you get the number you add to the x-coordinate (or y-coordinate) each time as you move to the right in a row of the table. For example, for segment $\underline{AC}$ the difference in the x-coordinates of A and C is $4 - 1 = 3$ and $3 \div 3 = 1$. This number 1 is the value that all the x-coordinates of the points in this row differ by 1.

e. In general, the points dividing a given $\overline{PZ}$ from (x_1, y_1) to (x_2, y_2) in thirds will have coordinates $(\frac{x_2 - x_1}{3} + x_1, \frac{y_2 - y_1}{3} + y_1)$ and $[2(\frac{x_2 - x_1}{3}) + x_1, 2(\frac{y_2 - y_1}{3}) + y_1]$. In a similiar form, the coordinates are $\left(\frac{2x_1 + x_2}{3}, \frac{2y_1 + y_2}{3}\right)$ and $\left(\frac{x_1 + 2x_2}{3}, \frac{y_1 + 2y_2}{3}\right)$.

65. Statement (D) is not true. The area ratio is 1 to 9, since the scale factor of similarity will be 3.

66. a. Since we know that the scale factor of each side to the corresponding side is 2, the triangles must be similar.

b. Suppose we extend segment SR to the left and add a point D to the left of the figure. Then $\angle ZSR \cong \angle WSD$. (They are vertical angles.) Then $\angle ZSR \cong \angle WSD \cong \angle SWY$. So, by the Alternate Interior Angles Theorem, SR is parallel to WY.

c. The argument would be identical to part (b) using $\triangle PXQ$ and $\triangle WXY$.

d. Lines parallel to the same line are parallel to each other.

e. Connect points X and Z with a diagonal and repeat the argument.

f. If opposite sides of a quadrilateral are parallel in pairs, the figure is, by definition, a parallelogram.

Figure 1

Segment	Endpoint	Dividing Point	Dividing Point	Endpoint
$\overline{AC}$	A (1, 1)	X (2, 4)	Y (3, 7)	C (4, 10)
$\overline{BC}$	B (10, 4)	M (8, 6)	N (6, 8)	C (4, 10)
$\overline{AB}$	A (1, 1)	P (4, 2)	Q (7, 3)	B (10, 4)

Possible Answers to Mathematical Reflections

1. **a.** The equation $x^2 + y^2 = r^2$ describes a circle of radius r that is centered at the origin. For example, the equation $x^2 + y^2 = 25$ describes a circle of radius 5 centered at the origin. Even more specifically, the point $(3, 4)$ is on the circle of radius 5 because $3^2 + 4^2 = 5^2$.

    b. The inequality $x^2 + y^2 < r^2$ describes the points on the interior of a circle of radius r centered at the origin. For example, $x^2 + y^2 < 5^2$ describes points on the interior of a circle of radius 5 centered at the origin. Even more specifically, the point $(1, 2)$ is in the interior of the circle of radius 5 centered at the origin because $1^2 + 2^2 < 5^2$.

2. **a.** The lines will be parallel if $m = n$. For example, $y = 3x + 5$ and $y = 3x + 7$ will be parallel, since they have the same slope. They will have different y-intercepts.

    b. The lines will be perpendicular if $m = -\frac{1}{n}$. For example, the graphs of $y = 3x + 5$ and $y = -(\frac{1}{3})x + 5$ will be perpendicular lines.

3. The midpoint of the segment joining (a, b) and (c, d) will be the point $\left(\frac{a + c}{2}, \frac{b + d}{2}\right)$.

Investigation 2 — Linear Equations and Inequalities

Mathematical and Problem-Solving Goals

- Identify situations calling for systems of linear equations and related inequalities
- Write systems of linear equations and related inequalities algebraically
- Interpret algebraic systems geometrically
- Use graphs to estimate solutions to systems of linear inequalities
- Identify questions that involve linear inequalities in one variable
- Develop techniques for working with inequalities and finding their solutions
- Solve linear inequalities in one variable
- Use a number line to represent solutions to inequalities in one variable

Many mathematicians believe that inequalities are at the heart of mathematics. To quote Beckenbach and Bellman from their book, *An Introduction to Inequalities* (1961, Yale), "the fundamental results of mathematics are often *inequalities* rather than *equalities*."

This investigation provides an opportunity for students to begin to explore the utility and power of inequalities in mathematics.

Summary of Problems

Problem 2.1 Graphs of Linear Systems

Prepares students for the geometric interpretation of algebraic systems that will follow in the next investigation.

Problem 2.2 Linear Inequalities

Builds on the system work in 2.1 to raise questions that involve linear inequalities in one variable. It develops ideas about reasoning with inequalities and their use in finding solutions of inequality problems such as $ax + b < cx + d$. This connects to work with linear equations.

Problem 2.3 Solving Linear Inequalities

Direct students' attention to systematic methods for solving linear inequalities in one variable and number line graphs of those solutions. The problem also connects to graphs of $y = mx + b$ as an alternative way of visualizing solutions for inequalities in one variable.

	Suggested Pacing	Materials for Students	Materials for Teachers	ACE Assignments
All	4 days	graph paper		
2.1	1 day		Transparencies 2.1A, 2.1B	1–6, 13–28
2.2	1 day		Transparency 2.2	7, 29–43, 58
2.3	$1\frac{1}{2}$ days		Transparencies 2.3A, 2.3B	8–12, 44–57, 59, 60
MR	$\frac{1}{2}$ day			

Goals

- Identify situations calling for systems of linear equations and related inequalities

- Write systems of linear equations and related inequalities

- Use graphs to estimate solutions to systems of linear inequalities

Launch 2.1

Discuss the information at the beginning of the investigation. Describe the two security companies. Ask students how they would make decisions about which security company to choose. These ideas should be very familiar from their work in *Moving Straight Ahead*.

Look at the Getting Ready with students. The purpose of this warm-up activity is to give you a sense of how facile students are in recognizing and thinking about linear functions, not to completely answer all the questions. Thus it makes sense in the whole-class discussion of these launching questions to simply get general student ideas of how they would go about answering the questions, then send them off to work on the detailed questions in Problem 2.1.

Suggested Questions

- *What kinds of equations will show how costs for each service are a function of number of days covered by the proposed security contract?* (The basic patterns of the two cost plans suggest linear functions because of the constant per day charges in each case. The actual rules are Super Locks: $y = 3,975 + 6x$ and Fail Safe: $y = 995 + 17.95x$. This problem is similiar to problems studied in previous units; *Moving Straight Ahead, Thinking With Mathematical Models,* and *Say It With Symbols.*)

If students are able to tell you these rules immediately, they are ahead of the game a bit, but you don't need to stay with this question until the whole class gets it.

- *If you graph the equations, what patterns would you expect to see?* [The graphs will be intersecting straight lines (because they will have different slopes). Super Locks will have a higher *y*-intercept, but rise more slowly than Fail Safe.]

- *How could you use the graph patterns to answer questions about best cost for the security service?* (To see which service is the better deal, you'll need to see which graph is lower for the number of days in the contract. For a few days, Fail Safe is less expensive, but once the two graphs intersect, Super Locks becomes less expensive.)

You might ask students to work in pairs on the problem, leading into the exploration with words like, "the detailed questions in Problem 2.1 will help you analyze the comparative costs of the two services for contract periods of different lengths."

Have students work in small groups, but each student should answer all of the questions.

Explore 2.1

Encourage students to make estimates instead of calculations in Question A—in this part of the problem, we are encouraging the use of the graphical representation. As you circulate to observe student work you might check to see that they are reaching correct answers for parts (1)–(4) and ask them to explain how they know they are right in some cases.

Question A, part (5) will require some more significant reasoning. Students will need to figure out a per–day charge for Fail Safe that will keep the cost for 500 days less than or equal to $7,000. Students might reason to get to that result in a variety of ways—from guess-and-test to figuring the slope of a line that starts at (0, 995) and goes through (500, 7,000).

Students might not immediately know how to write calculations or equations with solutions that will answer Question A, parts (1)–(4). You might need to help some students a bit by asking them to see if there is a way they can use their results from Question B to express the questions in symbolic form—replacing words or phrases by expressions and/or equal or inequality symbols. Students will probably not readily use inequalities to express the *less than* questions. But they will probably be able to express related equality conditions and then use those results to reason to the *less than* answers. The main point of this problem is to highlight the need for algebraic methods to deal with inequality questions. You should not stop to develop methods for systematic solution of inequalities at this point.

Going Further: Solve Question A parts (2) and (3) symbolically.

Summarize 2.1

Have students share their results. Ask students to comment on the relative usefulness of graphs and equations. In what circumstances would an estimate be good enough? When would you need an exact answer?

In particular, it will be helpful to have students explain how they can answer *less than* questions by reasoning from results of related equations. Have students lay out techniques they have found for solving inequalities.

Suggested Questions

- *What change would you make in the symbolic equation you wrote for Question A(1) in order to write Question A(2) symbolically?* (Change the $=$ sign to a $<$ sign.)

- *Can you use the same symbolic process you used for Question A(1) to find a solution symbolically for Question A(2)?* (Students may suggest solving the equation in Question A(1) first and then checking values of x around that solution to see what works for Question A(2). Or they may assume that the same steps will work for inequalities as for equations.)

2.1 Graphs of Linear Systems

Mathematical Goals

- Identify situations calling for systems of linear equations and related inequalities
- Write systems of linear equations and related inequalities
- Use graphs to estimate solutions to systems of linear equations and related inequalities

Launch

Describe the two security companies.

- *How would you make decisions about which security company to choose?*

Use the Getting Ready to get general student ideas of how they would go about answering the questions.

- *What kinds of equations will show how costs for each service are a function of number of days covered by the proposed security contract?*
- *If you graph the equations, what patterns would you expect to see? How could you use the graph patterns to answer questions about best cost for the security service?*
- *The detailed questions in Problem 2.1 will help you analyze the comparative costs of the two services for contract periods of different lengths*

Ask students to work in pairs on the problem.

Materials

- Transparencies 2.1A, 2.1B

Explore

Encourage students to make estimates instead of calculations in Question A—in this problem, we are encouraging the use of the graphical representation.

In Question A, part (5), students will need to figure out a per-day charge for Fail Safe that will keep the cost for 500 days less than or equal to $7,000. Students might reason to get to that result in a variety of ways—from guess-and-test to figuring the slope of a line that starts at (0, 995) and goes through (500, 7,000).

For students having trouble with Question C, ask if there is a way they can use their results from Question B to express the questions in symbolic form—replacing words or phrases by expressions and/or equal or inequality symbols. Students may not readily use inequalities to express the *less than* questions. The main focus is to highlight the need for algebraic methods to deal with inequality questions and not to develop methods for systematic solution of inequalities.

Have students share their results. Ask students to comment on the relative usefulness of graphs and equations.

- *In what circumstances would an estimate be good enough? When would you need an exact answer?*

In particular, it will be helpful to have students explain how they can answer *less than* questions by reasoning from results of related equations.

Materials
- Student notebooks

ACE Assignment Guide for Problem 2.1

Differentiated Instruction
Solutions for All Learners

Core 1–6, 13–22
Other *Applications* 23–28 and unassigned choices from previous problems

Adapted For suggestions about adapting Exercise 1 and other ACE exercises, see the CMP *Special Needs Handbook*.
Connecting to Prior Units 13–28: *Moving Straight Ahead*

Answers to Problem 2.1

A. Estimates based on the graphs

1. About 250 days and about $5,500

2. Any contract length greater than about 250 days

3. Any contract length less than about 340 days

4. About $7,500

5. The per-day charge must be less than about $12 because they would want their charge graph to start at $(0, 995)$ and pass through the point $(500, 7,000)$, giving a slope of about 12.

B. Super Locks: $c = 3,975 + 6d$
Fail Safe: $c = 995 + 17.95d$

C. To answer Question A, part (1): Solve $3,975 + 6d = 995 + 17.95d; d = 249.3$. Calculate $3,975 + 6(249.3) = 5,470.80$
To answer Question A, part (4): Calculate $995 + 17.95(365) = c; c = \$7,546.75$.

2.2 Linear Inequalities

Goals

- Identify questions involving linear inequalities in one variable
- Develop techniques for working with inequalities and in finding their solutions

Launch 2.2

Work through the Getting Ready questions as a whole class.

Suggested Questions

- *What would solving the equation 3,975 + 6d = 995 + 17.95d tell us?* (When the two costs are equal.)

- *Look at the three solution steps. What reasoning justifies each one?* (The first is justified because each of the expressions on the left and right sides of the equation are equal to c, the cost. So setting them equal makes an equation that asks us to find the one value of d that makes the two costs equal. The second is justified by the subtraction of equals from both sides of the equation: 995 and 6d are subtracted in the same step. The third step is justified by the division by equal (non-zero) quantities: 11.95.)

- *What is the overall strategy that guides the solution process?* (The aim is to get the unknown on one side of the equation and the number on the other.)

- *How do I know I can take all of these steps?* (Properties of equality.)

- *What does the statement d ≈ 249 tell you?* (That a value of d that is approximately 249 satisfies the equation. This means that for a contract of about 249 days, the two companies have the same cost.)

- *What does the solution tell you about the contract lengths that will be less expensive at Super Locks than at Fail Safe?* (For shorter contracts, the cost will be less expensive at Fail Safe. For longer contracts, the cost will be less at Super Locks.)

- *What does this tell about solutions to the inequality 3,975 + 6d < 995 + 17.95d?* (That values of days greater than 249 will satisfy the inequality.)

- *In this problem, we're going to explore some properties of inequalities.*

Use the preceding conversation to lead into a discussion of operations on inequalities. Ask students whether they think the exact same rules apply to inequalities as to equations. Tell them to keep an eye open for differences as they work on the problem.

Arrange students in groups of 2 or 3 for the problem.

Explore 2.2

You might choose to do Question A with the class after asking the Launch questions. Then put students in groups to do Questions B and C. OR, if you choose to put students in groups for Questions A–C, then, as you circulate, make sure that students recognize why Question A, parts (4) and (6) do not result in a true inequality. If they are struggling with those, try using specific numerical values for q and r. For example, in Question A, part (4), suppose q is −4 and r is −2. Then −4 < −2. But 24 (−4 times −6) is greater than 12 (−2 times −6).

Some students may find it enlightening to consider q and r with opposite signs. For example, if q = −2 and r = 2, then q < r. But then −6q = 12 and −6r = −12, so −6q > −6r.

Summarize 2.2

Go over Questions A and B with students. Invite student conjectures and arguments about why we can add and subtract negative numbers from both sides of an inequality without changing the inequality, but with multiplication we have to be more careful.

INVESTIGATION 2

Consider the operations on a number line. If we add or subtract values to A and B (pictured below), A and B shift left or right on the number line but stay in the same place relative to one another.

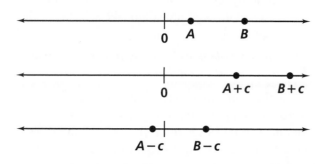

If we multiply by a positive number, A and B get further from zero (if the multiplier is greater than 1), or closer to zero (if the multiplier is less than 1). But they are in the same relative order.

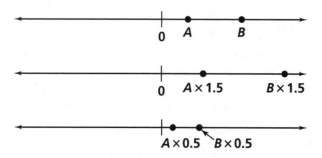

If we multiply by a negative number, A and B get further or closer to zero, as above, but they also switch signs. Most importantly, the order is reversed.

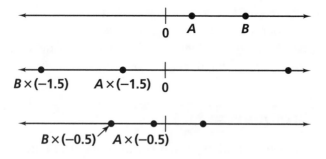

You might demonstrate this on the overhead and have students discuss the effect of each operation. Students may see connections back to the unit *Stretching and Shrinking* in grade 7. Note that division by a number, x, is the same as multiplying by $\frac{1}{x}$, so the discussion above applies to division as well.

Wrap up by discussing students' solutions to Question C. In particular, highlight two strategies for working with the inequalities in this part. In one strategy (on the left, below), we need to divide by a negative value and reverse the inequality sign. In the other strategy (on the right), we avoid this by keeping the coefficient positive.

$$
\begin{array}{ll}
3W + 12 < 5W - 4 \qquad & 3W + 12 < 5W - 4 \\
-2W + 12 < -4 & 12 < 2W - 4 \\
\quad -2W < -16 & 16 < 2W \\
\quad\quad W > 8 & 8 < W
\end{array}
$$

2.2 Linear Inequalities

Mathematical Goals

- Identify questions involving linear inequalities in one variable
- Develop techniques for working with inequalities and in finding their solutions

Launch

Ask students to describe the strategies they used in Problem 2.1 to figure out when Super Locks would be less expensive than Fail Safe. You might ask:

- *How could we express the question: "For what contract length will Super Locks cost less than Fail Safe?" symbolically?*
- *What would solving the equation $3,975 + 6d = 995 + 17.95d$ tell us?*
- *How can we solve the equation? How do I know I can take all of these steps?*
- *In this problem, we're going to explore some properties of inequalities.*

You might do Question A together as a class and arrange students in groups to work on B and C. OR, you might have students work in groups on Questions A–C.

Materials
- Transparency 2.2

Vocabulary
- system of linear equations

Explore

As you circulate, make sure that students recognize why Question A, parts (4) and (6) are not true. If they are struggling with those, try using specific numerical values for q and r. For example, in Question A, part (4), suppose q is -4 and r is -2. Then $-4 < -2$. But 24 is greater than 12.

Summarize

Go over Questions B and C with students. Invite student conjectures and arguments about why we can add and subtract negative numbers from both sides of an inequality without changing the inequality, but with multiplication we have to be more careful.

Consider the operations on a number line—including the cases of addition and subtraction, multiplication by a positive number > 1, by a positive number < 1, and by negative numbers both greater and less than -1.

Materials
- Student notebooks

Vocabulary
- Linear inequality

ACE Assignment Guide for Problem 2.2

Core 7

Other *Applications* 29–43, *Extensions* 58, and unassigned choices from previous problems

Adapted For suggestions about adapting ACE exercises, see the CMP *Special Needs Handbook*.
Connecting to Prior Units 13, 14, 16–18, 29–34, 36–41: *Accentuate the Negative*; 19–28: *Say It With Symbols*; 42: *Covering and Surrounding*; 43: *What Did You Expect?*

Answers to Problem 2.2

A. Examples will vary.

 1. $q + 23 < r + 23$. True

 2. $q - 35 < r - 35$. True

 3. $14q < 14r$. True

 4. $-6q < -6r$. False. If $q = 1, r = 2$, we get $-6q = -6$ and $-6r = -12$, but -6 is not less than -12. In fact, the statement is false for all q and r such that $q < r$

 5. $\frac{q}{5} < \frac{r}{5}$. true

 6. $\frac{q}{-3} < \frac{r}{-3}$ False. Using the values for q and r in number 4, $-\frac{1}{3}$ is not less than $-\frac{2}{3}$.

B. When working with equations, it doesn't matter if you multiply or divide by a negative number or a positive number. When working with inequalities, if you multiply or divide by a negative number, the inequality changes direction. In the case of both inequalities and equations, you can always add or subtract a number from both sides without affecting the inequality.

C. 1. $x = 8$

 2. $w > 8$

 3. $q = -3$

 4. $r < -3$

2.3 Solving Linear Inequalities

Goals

- Use systematic methods for solving linear inequalities in one variable
- Make number line graphs of solutions to linear inequalities

Launch 2.3

Launch this problem by discussing the Getting Ready.

Help students understand that the number line diagrams are simply a tool for representing solutions to inequalities and that inequalities generally have a range of solutions, unlike linear equations, which tend to have a single solution.

You might start students off with a focusing statement something like this: "You've seen in Problems 2.1 and 2.2 that inequality questions are similar in many ways to those that involve equations; but there are some specific cautions that have to be exercised in algebraic reasoning with inequalities. Keep those similarities and differences in mind to work on the questions of Question A."

Question B is included because it is a natural continuation of Question A, but consider it optional, or, for students who finish Question A early, or for an extension homework assignment.

Have students work in pairs.

Explore 2.3

As you circulate, ask students to explain reasoning and strategies as well as their results. After students do Question A, if you want to do Question B in class, you might bring students together for another launch. You can have a productive summary discussion when most students have completed most of Question A.

Summarize 2.3

Have students share their work. You might also ask them whether they think that the number line picture is helpful and why or why not.

If you assigned Question B, discuss it with the students.

Suggested Questions

- *What does the line* $y_2 = 1$ *tell you about the point where it crosses the line* $y_1 = 2x - 3$?
- *Can you write an equation that shows this?* $(1 = 2x - 3)$
- *What is the* x-*value of the point of intersection* (x, 1)? [x = 2. The intersection point is (2, 1).]
- *What will the* x-*values be that give you a value of* 2x − 3 *that is less than 1?* (x < 2)

2.3 Solving Linear Inequalities

Mathematical Goals

- Use systematic methods for solving linear inequalities in one variable
- Make number line graphs of solutions to linear inequalities

Launch

Launch this problem by discussing the Getting Ready box.

Help students understand that the number line diagrams are simply a tool for representing solutions to inequalities and that inequalities generally have a range of solutions, unlike linear equations, which tend to have a single solution.

You might start students off with a focusing statement something like this: "You've seen in Problems 2.1 and 2.2 that inequality questions are similar in many ways to those that involve equations; but there are some specific cautions that have to be exercised in algebraic reasoning with inequalities. Keep those similarities and differences in mind to work on the questions of Question A."

Question B is included because it is a natural continuation of Question A, but consider it optional, or, for students who finish Question A early, or for an extension homework assignment.

Have students work in pairs.

Materials
- Transparencies 2.3A, 2.3B

Explore

As you circulate, ask students to explain reasoning and strategies as well as their results. After students do Question A, if you want to do Question B in class, you might bring students together for another launch. You can have a productive summary discussion when most students have completed most of Question A.

Summarize

Have students share their work. You might also ask them whether they think that the number line picture is helpful and why or why not.

If you assigned Question B, discuss it with the students.

- *What does the line $y_2 = 1$ tell you about the point where it crosses the line $y_1 = 2x - 3$?*
- *Can you write an equation that shows this?*
- *What is the x-value of the point of intersection (x, 1)?*
- *What will the x-values be that give you a value of $2x - 3$ that is less than 1?*

Materials
- Student notebooks

ACE Assignment Guide for Problem 2.3

Differentiated Instruction
Solutions for All Learners

Core 8–11

Other 12, 44–57, 59, 60, and unassigned choices from previous problems

Adapted For suggestions about adapting ACE exercises, see the CMP *Special Needs Handbook*.
Connecting to Prior Units 15, 22: *Say It With Symbols*; 16: *Accentuate the Negative;* 17: *Moving Straight Ahead;* 19–21: *Frogs, Fleas, and Painted Cubes*

Answers to Problem 2.3

A. 1. $x < 10$

2. $6.5 < x$

3. $x > -2\frac{2}{3}$

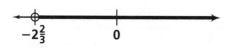

4. $x < 4$

5. $-4 > x$

6. approx. $249.37 < d$

B. 1. Luisa's solution for $2x - 3 = 1$ is $x = 2$. This corresponds to the x-coordinate of the point of intersection of $y = 2x - 3$ and $y = 1$.

2. Asking "For what value of x is $2x - 3 \le 1$?" is equivalent to asking, "For what values of x are the y-values given by $y = 2x - 3$ less than the y-values given by $y = 1$?" Instead of seeking the point of intersection as in Question B. 1, we now want all those x-values that make the line $y = 2x - 3$ "lower than" the line $y = 1$. These are the x-values to the left of and including $x = 2$.

3. For what x is it true that $y = 2x - 3$ is greater than $y = 1$? $x > 2$.

4. Answers will vary. Sample answer to Queston A, part (5): $y_1 = 18$, $y_2 = -4x + 2$. This is satisfied for $x < -4$, which is where the points for y_2 are higher than those for y_1.

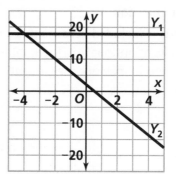

The student edition pages for this investigation begin on the next page.

Notes _____

_____

_____

_____

Linear Equations and Inequalities

Connecting geometry and algebra can help you solve problems. In the last Investigation, you used algebra to describe and reason about geometric shapes in the coordinate plane. Now, you will use coordinate geometry to help you think about algebraic equations and inequalities.

Suppose the managers of a shopping center want to upgrade their security system. Two providers bid for the job.

- Super Locks will charge $3,975 to install the equipment and then $6.00 per day to monitor the system and respond to alerts.

- Fail Safe will charge $995 to install the equipment and then $17.95 per day to monitor the system and respond to alerts.

Both companies are reliable and capable, so the choice comes down to cost.

Getting Ready for Problem 2.1

- What kinds of equations will show how the costs for the two companies are a function of the number of days?

- What patterns do you expect to see in graphs of the equations?

- How can you use a graph to answer questions about which company offers the best price?

2.1 Graphs of Linear Systems

The cost of the security services from Super Locks and Fail Safe depends on the number of days the company provides service. The graph below shows the bids for both companies.

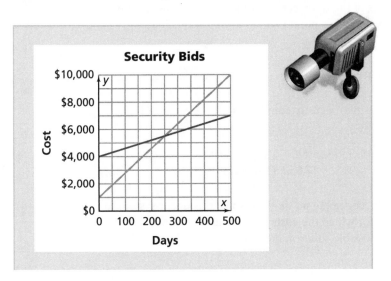

Security Bids

Problem 2.1 Graphs of Linear Systems

A. Use the graphs to estimate the answers to these questions. Explain your reasoning in each case.

  1. For what number of days will the costs for the two companies be the same? What is that cost?

  2. For what numbers of days will Super Locks cost less than Fail Safe?

  3. For what numbers of days will Super Locks cost less than $6,000?

  4. What is the cost of one year of service from Fail Safe?

  5. How can Fail Safe adjust its per-day charge to make its cost for 500 days of service cheaper than Super Locks' cost?

B. For each company, write an equation for the cost c for d days of security services.

C. For parts (1) and (4) of Question A, write an equation you can solve to answer the question. Then use symbolic methods to find the exact answers.

ACE Homework starts on page 30.

Notes _____

_____

_____

_____

2.2 Linear Inequalities

In Problem 2.1, you used graphic and symbolic methods to analyze a **system of linear equations.** The problem conditions could be expressed as two equations relating security costs and the number of days for the business contract. The coordinates of the intersection point of the graphs satisfied both equations in the system. This point is the *solution* of the system.

Getting Ready for Problem 2.2

The cost equations for the two security companies are a system of linear equations:

$$c = 3{,}975 + 6d \quad \text{(Super Locks)}$$
$$\text{and} \quad c = 995 + 17.95d \quad \text{(Fail Safe)}$$

In previous units, you learned some methods to solve this linear system to find the number of days for which the costs are the same for both companies. Here is one possible solution method:

$$3{,}975 + 6d = 995 + 17.95d \qquad (1)$$
$$2{,}980 = 11.95d \qquad (2)$$
$$249 \approx d \qquad (3)$$

- Give a reason for each step in the solution.
- What is the overall strategy that guides the solution process?
- What does the statement $d \approx 249$ tell you?
- How can the solution to this system help you answer this question: For what numbers of days will Super Locks cost less than Fail Safe?
- What does your answer to the previous question tell you about solutions to the inequality $3{,}975 + 6d < 995 + 17.95d$?

Notes _____

_____

_____

_____

It is fairly easy to find some solutions to an inequality. However, sometimes it is useful to find all the solutions by solving the inequality symbolically. The following problems will help you develop strategies for solving inequalities.

Problem 2.2 Linear Inequalities

A. For each instruction in parts (1)–(6), start with $q < r$. Tell whether performing the operation on $q < r$ will give an inequality that is still true. If so, explain why. If not, give specific examples to show why the resulting inequality is false.

1. Add 23 to both sides.

2. Subtract 35 from both sides.

3. Multiply both sides by 14.

4. Multiply both sides by -6.

5. Divide both sides by 5.

6. Divide both sides by -3.

B. What do your results from Question A suggest about how working with inequalities is similar to and different from working with equations?

C. Solve these equations and inequalities.

1. $3x + 12 = 5x - 4$ **2.** $3w + 12 < 5w - 4$

3. $q - 5 = 6q + 10$ **4.** $r - 5 > 6r + 10$

ACE Homework starts on page 30.

I need to end up with all the terms with variables on one side.

Notes _____

_____

_____

_____

2.3 Solving Linear Inequalities

Many practical problems require solving linear inequalities. You can reason about inequalities, such as $2x - 4 < 5$ or $2x - 4 > -0.5x + 1$, using both symbolic and graphic methods. Solutions to inequalities with one variable are generally given in the form $x < a$, $x > a$, $x \le a$, or $x \ge a$.

Getting Ready for Problem

- What are some values that satisfy the inequality $3x + 4 \le 13$?
- Describe all the solutions of the inequality $3x + 4 \le 13$.

All the solutions of $3x + 4 \le 13$ can be displayed in a number-line graph. This graph represents $x \le 3$, all x-values less than or equal to 3.

- Explain why the solutions of $3x + 4 < 13$ do *not* include the value 3.

The number-line graph below represents the solutions of $3x + 4 < 13$. It shows $x < 3$, all x-values strictly less than 3. The open circle shows that 3 is not a solution.

- Make a number-line graph showing the solutions of $2x - 4 < 5$.
- Explain in words what the graph tells about the solutions.

STUDENT PAGE

Notes _____

_____

_____

_____

A. Use symbolic reasoning to solve each inequality. Then make a number-line graph of the solutions. Be prepared to justify your solution steps and to explain your graphs.

1. $3x + 17 < 47$ **2.** $43 < 8x - 9$

3. $-6x + 9 < 25$ **4.** $14x - 23 < 5x + 13$

5. $18 < -4x + 2$ **6.** $3{,}975 + 6d < 995 + 17.95d$

B. Luisa wants to use her graphing calculator to solve $2x - 3 \le 1$. She graphs the linear functions $y = 2x - 3$ and $y = 1$. She uses an x- and a y-scale of 1.

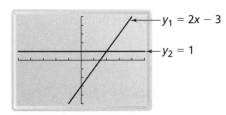

$y_1 = 2x - 3$

$y_2 = 1$

1. Luisa knows that the solution for $2x - 3 = 1$ is $x = 2$. How does this relate to the graphs of the lines she drew?

2. How do the graphs show that the solution of $2x - 3 \le 1$ is $x \le 2$?

3. How can you use the graph to find the solution of $2x - 3 > 1$? What is the solution?

4. For one of the inequalities in Question A, sketch a graph or use your graphing calculator to find the solution. Check that your solution agrees with the one you found by using symbolic reasoning.

ACE Homework starts on page 30.

STUDENT PAGE

Notes _____

_____

_____

_____

Applications

1. a. Sam needs to rent a car for a one-week trip in Oregon. He is considering two companies. A+ Auto Rental charges $175 plus $0.10 per mile. Zippy Auto Rental charges $220 plus $0.05 per mile. Write an equation relating the rental cost for each company to the miles driven.

   b. Graph the equations.

   c. Under what circumstances is the rental cost the same for both companies? What is that cost?

   d. Under what circumstances is renting from Zippy cheaper than renting from A+?

   e. Suppose Sam rents a car from A+ and drives it 225 miles. What is his rental cost?

2. Maggie lives 1,250 meters from school. Ming lives 800 meters from school. Both girls leave for school at the same time. Maggie walks at an average speed of 70 meters per minute, while Ming walks at an average speed of 40 meters per minute. Maggie's route takes her past Ming's house.

Homework Help Online
PHSchool.com
For: Help with Exercise 2
Web Code: ape-7202

   a. Write equations that show Maggie and Ming's distances from school t minutes after they leave their homes.

   Answer parts (b)–(d) by writing and solving equations or inequalities.

   b. When, if ever, will Maggie catch up with Ming?

   c. How long will Maggie remain behind Ming?

   d. At what times is the distance between the two girls less than 20 meters?

Notes _____

_____

_____

_____

For Exercises 3–6, graph the system of equations and estimate the point of intersection. Then use symbolic reasoning to check whether your estimate is accurate.

3. $y = 2x + 4$ and $y = \frac{1}{2}x - 2$ **4.** $y = x + 5$ and $y = -3x + 3$

5. $y = 3$ and $y = 6x - 3$ **6.** $x = 2$ and $y = -\frac{2}{5}x + 4$

7. Suppose s and t are two numbers and that $s > t$. Decide whether each inequality must be true.

a. $s + 15 > t + 15$ **b.** $s - (-22) > t - (-22)$

c. $s \times 0 > t \times 0$ **d.** $\frac{s}{-6} > \frac{t}{-6}$

e. $\frac{s}{6} > \frac{t}{6}$ **f.** $s \times -3 < t \times -4$

For Exercises 8–11, solve the inequality. Then, graph the solution on a number line.

Go Online
PHSchool.com
For: Multiple-Choice Skills Practice
Web Code: apa-7254

8. $12 < 7x - 2$ **9.** $2x + 12 > 32$

10. $4x - 17 \le 31$ **11.** $-16x - 12 > 14 - 10x$

12. Use these graphs to estimate solutions for the inequalities and equations in parts (a)–(f). Then, use symbolic reasoning to check your estimates.

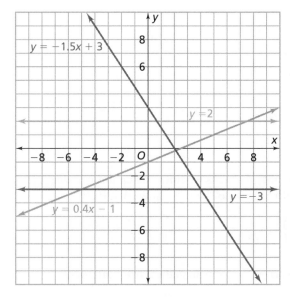

a. $0.4x - 1 > 2$ **b.** $0.4x - 1 > -3$

c. $-1.5x + 3 > 2$ **d.** $-1.5x + 3 < -3$

e. $-1.5x + 3 = 0.4x - 1$ **f.** $-1.5x + 3 > 0.4x - 1$

Investigation 2 Linear Equations and Inequalities   **31**

Notes _____

_____

_____

_____

Connections

Calculate the *y*-value for the given *x*-value.

13. $y = 3x + 2$ when $x = -2$

14. $y = -3x + 4$ when $x = 9$

15. $y = \frac{1}{2}x - 4$ when $x = 24$

16. $y = -5x - 7$ when $x = \frac{3}{15}$

17. $y = \frac{2}{3}x - 12$ when $x = -18$

18. $y = -\frac{1}{4}x - \frac{3}{4}$ when $x = -6$

Write an equation for the line satisfying the given conditions.

19. slope $= 2$, *y*-intercept $= -3$

20. slope $= -4$, passes through $(0, 1.5)$

21. passes through $(-2, 1)$ and $(4, -3)$

22. passes through $(4, 0)$ and $(0, 3)$

Identify the slope, *x*-intercept, and *y*-intercept of the line.

23. $y = 7x - 3$

24. $y = -3x + 4$

25. $y = \frac{2}{3}x + 12$

26. $y = -\frac{1}{4}x - 5$

27. $y = \frac{3}{4} - 17x$

28. $y = -\frac{3}{5}(x + 10)$

For Exercises 29–34, copy each pair of expressions. Insert <, >, or = to make a true statement.

29. $-18 \div -3 \ \blacksquare \ -24 \div -4$

30. $1{,}750(-12) \ \blacksquare \ (1{,}749)(-12)$

31. $5(18 - 24) \ \blacksquare \ 90 - (-120)$

32. $-8(-5) \ \blacksquare \ (-7)(-5)$

33. $4(-3 - (-7)) \ \blacksquare \ 4(-3) - 4(-7)$

34. $-5(-4)^2 \ \blacksquare \ -4(-5)^2$

35. Write an equation or inequality that tells whether each point is inside, outside, or on the circle with a radius of 10 and centered at $(0, 0)$.

    a. $(6, 8)$
    b. $(7, 7)$
    c. $(-7, -7)$

    d. $(-6, 8)$
    e. $(-7, 8)$
    f. $(-7, -8)$

Copy each pair of fractions. Insert <, >, or = to make a true statement.

36. $\frac{6}{8} \ \blacksquare \ \frac{-18}{24}$

37. $\frac{6}{8} \ \blacksquare \ \frac{7}{9}$

38. $\frac{6}{8} \ \blacksquare \ \frac{-7}{9}$

39. $\frac{6}{8} \ \blacksquare \ \frac{-18}{-24}$

40. $\frac{6}{8} \ \blacksquare \ \frac{-7}{-9}$

41. $\frac{8}{6} \ \blacksquare \ \frac{-9}{-7}$

Notes _____

_____

_____

_____

42. Use these figures for parts (a)–(f). Insert $<$, $=$, or $>$ to make true statements.

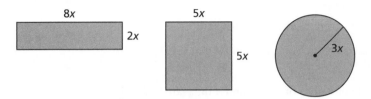

- **a.** perimeter of square ■ perimeter of rectangle
- **b.** area of square ■ area of rectangle
- **c.** perimeter of square ■ circumference of circle
- **d.** area of square ■ area of circle
- **e.** perimeter of rectangle ■ circumference of circle
- **f.** area of rectangle ■ area of circle

43. The gender of a newborn child is nearly equally likely to be a boy or a girl. Consider the patterns likely to occur in a family with three children.

Copy parts (a)–(d). Insert $<$, $=$, or $>$ to make true statements.

- **a.** P(all boys) ■ P(all girls)
- **b.** P(exactly one boy) ■ P(exactly 2 girls)
- **c.** P(BGB) ■ P(BBG)
- **d.** P(two boys and one girl) ■ P(all girls)

Notes _____

_____

_____

_____

44. Multiple Choice If $w = 3x + c$, what is the value of x?

A. 3   **B.** $\frac{w - c}{3}$ **C.** $w - c$ **D.** $\frac{w + c}{3}$

45. Suppose $\frac{a}{b}$ and $\frac{c}{d}$ are two non-zero fractions and $\frac{a}{b} < \frac{c}{d}$.

     a. Give an example of values of a, b, c, and d that satisfy $\frac{a}{b} < \frac{c}{d}$ and also $\frac{b}{a} < \frac{d}{c}$.

     b. Give an example of values of a, b, c, and d that satisfy $\frac{a}{b} < \frac{c}{d}$ and also $\frac{b}{a} > \frac{d}{c}$.

46. Multiple Choice Which equation's graph is perpendicular to the graph of $y = 2.5x + 4$?

     F. $y = 2.5x$ **G.** $y = 0.4x$ **H.** $y = -0.4x$ **J.** $y = -2.5x$

47. Multiple Choice For which set of points is one point the midpoint of the segment joining the other two points?

     A. $(0, 0)$, $(5, 6)$, $(10, 3)$ **B.** $(0, 3)$, $(2, 6)$, $(-2, 0)$

     C. $(4, 6)$, $(8, 12)$, $(16, 24)$ **D.** $(2, 0)$, $(2, 6)$, $(2, -3)$

48. Use a table or graph of $y = 5(2^x)$ to estimate the solution of the inequality $5(2^x) > 1{,}000$.

49. Use a table or graph of $y = x^2 - x - 6$ to estimate the solution of the inequality $x^2 - x - 6 < 0$.

For Exercises 50–54, write the equation in factored form. Then, use the equation to find the x- and y-intercepts for the graph of the equation.

50. $y = x^2 + 4x$ **51.** $y = x^2 + 4x + 4$ **52.** $y = x^2 + 3x - 10$

53. $y = x^2 - 8x + 16$ **54.** $y = x^2 - 4$ **55.** $y = x^2 + 4x + 3$

56. Multiple Choice Which expression is the factored form of $1x + 2x + 6$?

     F. $3x + 6$ **G.** $2(x + 3)$ **H.** $3(x + 2)$ **J.** $3(x + 6)$

Notes _____

_____

_____

_____

Extensions

57. In parts (a)–(d), find values of x that satisfy the given conditions. Then, graph the solution on a number line.

    a. $x + 7 < 4$ *or* $x + 3 > 9$ (That is, find the x-values that satisfy one inequality or the other or both.)

    b. $3x + 4 < 13$ *and* $12 < 6x$ (That is, find x-values that satisfy both inequalities.)

    c. $5x - 6 > 2x + 18$ *or* $-3x + 5 > 8x - 39$

    d. $-11x - 7 < -7x + 33$ *and* $9 + 2x > 11x$

58. Suppose m and n are positive whole numbers and $m < n$. Tell whether each statement is always true.

    a. $2^m < 2^n$ **b.** $m^2 < n^2$ **c.** $0.5^m < 0.5^n$ **d.** $\frac{1}{m} < \frac{1}{n}$

59. Solve these quadratic inequalities.

    a. $5x^2 + 7 \leq 87$

    b. $5x^2 + 7 > 87$

60. Solve these exponential inequalities.

    a. $2(3^x) - 8 < 46$

    b. $2(3^x) - 8 > 10$

Hint:

Use a graph or table of $y = 5x^2 + 7$ for Exercise 59, and a graph or table of $y = 2x(3^x) - 8$ for Exercise 60, to estimate the solutions. Then adapt the reasoning used to solve linear inequalities to check the accuracy of your estimates.

Notes _____

_____

_____

_____

Mathematical Reflections 2

In this investigation, you learned graphic and symbolic methods for solving systems of linear equations and linear inequalities. These questions will help you summarize what you have learned.

Think about your answers to these questions. Discuss your ideas with other students and your teacher. Then write a summary of your findings in your notebook.

1. How can you use coordinate graphs to solve linear equations such as $ax + b = cx + d$ and linear inequalities such as $ax + b < cx + d$?

2. **a.** How can you use symbolic reasoning to solve inequalities such as $ax + b < c$?

   b. How can you use symbolic reasoning to solve inequalities such as $ax + b < cx + d$?

Notes _____

_____

_____

_____

Answers

Applications Connections Extensions

Investigation ②

ACE
Assignment Choices

Problem 2.1
Core 1–6, 13–22
Other 23–28 and unassigned choices from previous problems

Problem 2.2
Core 7
Other 29–43, 58, and unassigned choices from previous problems

Problem 2.3
Core 8–11
Other 12, 44–57, 59, 60, and unassigned choices from previous problems

Adapted For suggestions about adapting Exercise 1 and other ACE exercises, see the CMP *Special Needs Handbook*.
Connecting to Prior Units 7–9, 17: *Moving Straight Ahead*; 13, 14, 16–18, 29–34, 36–41: *Accentuate the Negative*; 19–28: *Say It With Symbols*; 19–21: *Frogs, Fleas and Painted Cubes*; 42: *Covering and Surrounding*; 43: *What Did You Expect?*

Applications

1. a. A+: $175 + 0.10x = c$
   Zippy: $220 + 0.05x = c$

b.

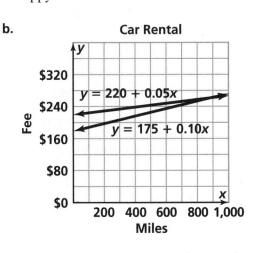

c. 900 miles, $265

d. Zippy will be cheaper for distances greater than 900 miles.

e. If the car is driven 225 miles, A+ rental will charge $197.50.

2. a. Maggie: $d = 1250 - 70t$
   Ming: $d = 800 - 40t$

b. $1{,}250 - 70t = 800 - 40t$;
   solution $t = 15$ minutes

c. less than 15 minutes

d. Answers will vary. If we use a graph of the equation in part (a), we have

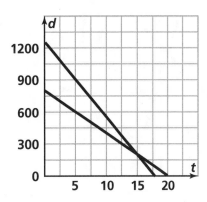

We know that the intersection point is at $t = 15$ min. Checking other values:

t	Distance Between Girls
14	$270 - 240 = 30$
14.5	$235 - 220 = 15$
15	$200 - 200 = 0$
15.5	$180 - 165 = 15$
16	$160 - 130 = 30$

We can say that at $t = 14.5$ or $t = 15.5$, the distance is less than 20 m.

Investigation 2 Linear Equations and Inequalities **51**

3–6. Symbolic reasoning will vary. An example is shown for Exercise 3.

3. $(-4, -4)$

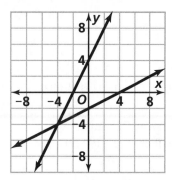

Check: $2x + 4 = \frac{1}{2}x - 2$

$$1.5x = -6$$
$$x = -4$$
$$y = 2(-4) + 4 = -4$$

4. $(-\frac{1}{2}, \frac{9}{2})$

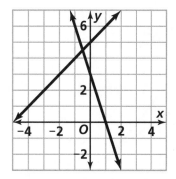

5. $(1, 3)$

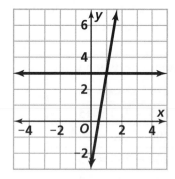

6. $(2, \frac{16}{5})$

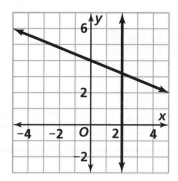

7. a. T   **b.** T   **c.** F

     d. F   **e.** T

     f. Can not be determined.

8. $2 < x$

9. $x > 10$

10. $x \le 12$

11. $x < -4\frac{1}{3}$

12. Symbolic reasoning will vary. An example is shown for part (a).

     a. $x > 7.5$; Check: $0.4x > 3$

                           $x > 7.5$

     b. $x > -5$ **c.** $x < \frac{2}{3}$ **d.** $x > 4$

     e. $x = \frac{40}{19}$ or approximately $x = 2.11$

     f. $x < \frac{40}{19}$ or approximately $x < 2.11$

Connections

13. −4   **14.** −23   **15.** 8   **16.** −8

17. −24   **18.** $\frac{3}{4}$

19. $y = 2x - 3$ **20.** $y = -4x + 1.5$

21. $y = -\frac{2}{3}x - \frac{1}{3}$ **22.** $y = -\frac{3}{4}x + 3$

23. slope = 7; y-intercept = $(0, -3)$;
x-intercept = $(\frac{3}{7}, 0)$

24. slope = −3; y-intercept = $(0, 4)$;
x-intercept = $(\frac{4}{3}, 0)$

25. slope = $\frac{2}{3}$; y-intercept = $(0, 12)$;
x-intercept = $(-18, 0)$

26. slope = $-\frac{1}{4}$; y-intercept = $(0, -5)$;
x-intercept = $(-20, 0)$

27. slope = −17; y-intercept = $(0, \frac{3}{4})$;
x-intercept = $(\frac{3}{68}, 0)$

28. slope = $-\frac{3}{5}$; y-intercept = $(0, -6)$;
x-intercept = $(-10, 0)$

29. =   **30.** <   **31.** <

32. >   **33.** =   **34.** >

35. a. on: $6^2 + 8^2 = 10^2$

  b. inside: $7^2 + 7^2 < 10^2$

  c. inside: $(-7)^2 + (-7)^2 < 10^2$

  d. on: $(-6)^2 + 8^2 = 10^2$

  e. outside: $(-7)^2 + 8^2 > 10^2$

  f. outside: $(-7)^2 + (-8)^2 > 10^2$

36. >   **37.** <   **38.** >

39. =   **40.** <   **41.** >

42. a. =   **b.** >   **c.** >

  d. <   **e.** >   **f.** <

43. a. =   **b.** =   **c.** =   **d.** >

44. B

45. Answers will vary. Some examples are:

  a. $-\frac{1}{2} < \frac{3}{4}$ and $\frac{2}{-1} < \frac{4}{3}$

  b. $\frac{1}{2} < \frac{3}{4}$ and $\frac{2}{1} > \frac{4}{3}$

46. Correct choice is H because $\frac{-1}{2.5} = -0.4$.

47. Correct choice is B; the midpoint is $(0, 3)$.

48. Solution of $5(2^x) > 1{,}000$ for approximately
$x > 7.64$; for integer solution set, the
inequality holds for $x > 7$.

49. $x^2 - x - 6 < 0$ for $-2 < x < 3$.

50. Factored form: $y = x(x + 4)$,
y-intercept: $(0, 0)$,
x-intercepts $(0, 0)$ and $(-4, 0)$

51. Factored form: $y = (x + 2)(x + 2)$,
y-intercept: $(0, 4)$, x-intercept $(-2, 0)$

52. Factored form: $y = (x - 2)(x + 5)$,
y-intercept: $(0, -10)$,
x-intercepts $(2, 0)$ and $(-5, 0)$

53. Factored form: $y = (x - 4)(x - 4)$,
y-intercept: $(0, 16)$, x-intercept $(4, 0)$

54. Factored form: $y = (x + 2)(x - 2)$,
y-intercept: $(0, -4)$,
x-intercepts $(-2, 0)$ and $(2, 0)$

55. Factored form: $y = (x + 1)(x + 3)$,
y-intercept: $(0, 3)$,
x-intercepts $(-1, 0)$ and $(-3, 0)$

56. H

Extensions

57. a. $x < -3$ or $x > 6$;

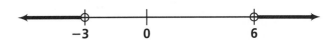

  b. $x < 3$ and $x > 2$;

  c. $x > 8$ or $x < 4$;

  d. $x > -10$ and $x < 1$;

58. a. True, because $n = m + k$ for some $k > 0$ and $2^k > 1$, so $2^m < 2^m 2^k = 2^n$.

b. True, because we can only look at positive whole numbers. The area of a square with side length m is smaller than the area of a square with side length n (where m and n are positive whole numbers and $m < n$).

c. Not true because repeated multiplication by 0.5 produces smaller and smaller numbers.

d. Not true when $m = 5$ and $n = 10$, for example.

59. a. $5x^2 + 7 \le 87$ when $-4 \le x \le 4$

b. $5x^2 + 7 > 87$ when $x < -4$ and when $x > 4$

60. a. $x < 3$ **b.** $x > 2$

Possible Answers to Mathematical Reflections

1. You can use a coordinate graph to solve a linear equation such as $ax + b = cx + d$ by graphing the two lines $y = ax + b$ and $y = cx + d$ and seeing where they intersect. To use a graph to solve inequalities of the form $ax + b < cx + d$, you would need to graph the two lines and see for which x-values the y-values given by $y = ax + b$ are less than ("lower than") the y-values given by $y = cx + d$.

2. The rules for solving inequalities are similar to but different in some ways from the rules for solving equations. You cannot necessarily "do the same thing to both sides" when working with inequalities. For example, you cannot simply divide both sides of an inequality by a negative number and get an equivalent inequality. To solve something such as $ax + b < cx + d$ symbolically, you could subtract d from both sides to get $ax + b - d < cx$. Then you could subtract ax from both sides (this is legitimate, even with inequalities) to get $b - d < cx - ax$. Then you could use the distributive property to write $b - d < x(c - a)$. If $c - a < 0$, you would have to write $\frac{b - d}{c - a} > x$ because you would be dividing by a negative number. If $c - a > 0$, you would write $\frac{b - d}{c - a} < x$.

Investigation 3 — Equations With Two or More Variables

Mathematical and Problem-Solving Goals

- Understand the $ax + by = c$ form of linear equations and the equivalence of those forms to equations in the form $y = mx + b$

- Analyze systems of linear equations graphically

- Gain fluency with symbol manipulation

Summary of Problems

Problem 3.1   Many Ways to Reach a Goal

Problem 3.1 introduces linear equations in "standard form," $ax + by = c$. Students are led to discover that graphs of solutions for such equations also turn out to be straight lines.

Problem 3.2   Connecting $y = mx + b$ and $ax + by = c$

Connects the $y = mx + b$ and $ax + by = c$ forms of linear equations. Useful strategies for connecting these two forms are revealed by asking students to analyze sample student work. The main algebraic properties needed in these cases are the distributive property and the general principle that equals can be added to, subtracted from, multiplied by, or divided into equals without changing the equality relationship.

Problem 3.3   Intersections of Lines

Introduces the concept of a system of linear equations and the graphic image of solving that system. Symbol-based algorithms for solving linear systems come in the next investigation.

	Suggested Pacing	Materials for Students	Materials for Teachers	ACE Assignments
All	4 days	graph paper		
3.1	1 day	Labsheet 3.1 (one per group)	Transparencies 3.1A, 3.1B	1–8, 28–35
3.2	1 day		Transparencies 3.2A, 3.2B	15–27, 36–50, 63
3.3	$1\frac{1}{2}$ days	Labsheet 3.3 (one per group)	Transparency 3.3	9–14, 51–62, 64, 65
MR	$\frac{1}{2}$ day			

Many Ways to Reach a Goal

Goal

- Introduce linear equations in two variables in standard form

Launch 3.1

Begin by describing the problem situation, which is quite similar to problems in the unit *Say It With Symbols*. Ask students to describe in words how much profit the class will make from each item in their sale. Clarify that *profit* and *selling price* are not the same.

Suggested Questions

- *What algebraic expression describes how much profit the eighth-graders will make by selling* s *shirts?* (5s, because the sale of each shirt brings $5 profit.)

- *What algebraic expression describes how much profit the eighth-graders will make by selling* c *caps?* (10c, because the sale of each cap brings $10 profit.)

Then use the Getting Ready to ask:

- *What equation shows how profit,* p, *is related to the number of shirts* s *and the number of caps* c *sold in the fund-raiser?* (5s + 10c = p.)

- *Let's practice using this equation. Find the profit when 30 shirts and 50 caps are sold.* ($650)

- *Find the profit when 15 shirts and 10 caps are sold ...when 12 shirts and 20 caps are sold.* ($175 and $260, respectively)

- *What might it mean to solve such an equation with three variables?* (Students may have various ideas about this. Find values of the variables that produce true statements; for example, $s = 8, c = 12$, and $p = 160$ constitute a solution of the equation with three variables.)

- *What ideas do you have for finding solutions of the equation?*

It seems likely that students will have only guess-and-test strategies at this point. This question gives you a chance to see what students are thinking. You can point out that the overall goal of this and the next investigation is to develop some systematic approaches to these questions.

You might also give students time to consider some alternate scenarios, with questions such as:

- *Can you find two different shirt/cap combinations that would yield the same profit?*

- *If the project has $600 profit and there were 10 T-shirts sold, how many caps were sold?*

Arrange students in groups of 2 to 3 to work on the problem.

Explore 3.1

Have students work on Questions A through C. You may want to bring the class together to discuss Question D as a whole class. As students work on the parts of this problem, check to see that in Question B they are actually producing numbers of shirts and caps that together produce the desired $600 profit.

If students are struggling, encourage them to begin with one of the variables (either caps or shirts) and to make guesses with numbers that make for easy calculations, such as multiples of 10.

It may be surprising to some students that they can use any value for the number of shirts, and that there will be a corresponding number of hats to satisfy the equation. Of course, some values of one variable will produce nonsensical values for the other (e.g., a negative number of shirts). You could challenge some students to solve various minimum and maximum problems.

Going Further

- *What is the largest number of shirts that could be sold to earn $600 profit?*

- *What is the largest number of caps?*

- *What is the largest number of units (i.e., caps and shirts combined) that can be sold to earn $600 profit?*

- *What is the smallest number of units?*

If you need yet a further challenge for some students, they could explore these kinds of questions a bit further:

Going Further

- *The largest number of units that could be sold to earn $600 profit was 120—all caps. If you sell 120 units, but include both caps and shirts, the profit will change. What would that equation look like?* [$p = 5s + 10c$, where $s + c = 120$, or $p = 5s + 10(120 - s)$.]

- *What would be the maximum (minimum) profit that can be made in this situation?*

Check to see that students have the correct plots in Question C before they go ahead to Question D.

Summarize 3.1

Although you likely checked students' work during the Explore time, revisit the graph for Question B at the beginning of the summary.

Ask students to share the graphs they found for Question C.

Suggested Questions

- *What do your results suggest about the likely graph shape for solutions to any equation that looks like* ax + by = c?

It is critical that students recognize and agree that graphs of all solutions to any particular equation of this form will be straight lines.

You can foreshadow the ideas of Problem 3.2 by asking,

- *Does this mean an equation in the form* ax + by = c *represents a linear relationship?*

- *How is this form different from what we have studied so far when we have studied linear relationships?*

- *What is the slope and y-intercept of the line?*

Do not linger on these questions now, as there will be time to focus on them in the next problem.

You might ask students to consider the differences between working with equations in one variable and working with equations in two variables by asking a question such as the following

- *How is solving 600 = 5s + 10c different from solving 600 = 5 + 10c?*

The first equation is in two variables, whereas the second has only one variable. In the first case, there is a set of solutions, ordered pairs. Together, these solutions form a line. In their prior work with linear equations in one variable, students could use a graph to solve, but the solution was a single point. If students think about manipulating $600 = 5s + 10c$, they find that the manipulation does not produce a numerical solution for either s or c. That is, if solved for s, we get $s = 120 - 2c$, which is still an equation in two variables. If solved for c, the same thing happens, with the result $c = 60 - 0.5s$.

3.1 Many Ways to Reach a Goal

Mathematical Goal

- Introduce linear equations in two variables in "standard form"

Launch

Begin by describing the problem situation.

Clarify the fact that profit and selling price are not the same.

- *What algebraic expression describes how much profit the eighth-graders will make by selling s shirts?*
- *What algebraic expression describes how much profit the eighth-graders will make by selling c caps?*

Discuss the Getting Ready:

- *What equation shows how profit, p, is related to the number of shirts s and the number of caps c sold in the fund-raiser?*
- *What might it mean to solve such an equation with three variables?*
- *What ideas do you have for finding solutions of the equation?*

Students may have only guess-and-test strategies at this point.

Materials

- Transparencies 3.1A, 3.1B
- Labsheet 3.1 (1 per group)

Explore

Have students work on Questions A through C. You may want to bring the class together to discuss Question D as a whole class group.

Check that in Question B they are actually producing numbers of shirts and caps that together produce the desired $600 profit.

To have the graphs reveal the linear pattern of solution points that is critical, encourage students to make some of their initial guesses use multiples of 10 only as numbers of caps and shirts.

Check that students have the correct plots in C before they go ahead to Question D.

Summarize

Revisit the graph from Question B.

Ask students to share the graphs they found for Question C.

- *What do your results suggest about the likely graph shape for solutions to any equation that looks like* ax + by = c?

It is critical that students recognize and agree that graphs of all solutions to any particular equation of this sort will be straight lines.

Foreshadow the ideas of Problem 3.2 by asking whether equations of this form represent linear relationships.

Materials

- Student notebooks

ACE Assignment Guide for Problem 3.1

Core 1–8, 28–35
Other Unassigned choices from previous problems

Adapted For suggestions about adapting Exercise 2 and other ACE exercises, see the CMP *Special Needs Handbook*.
Connecting to Prior Units 36–47: *Moving Straight Ahead*

Answers to Problem 3.1

A. $5s + 10c = 600$ is satisfied by ordered pairs (s, c) like these:
$(0, 60), (20, 50),$
$(40, 40), (60, 30),$
$(80, 20),$ and $(100, 10).$
Of course, there are many other possibilities.

B. 1. The graph (in the first quadrant, which is the only place where the variables make sense for the context) is below.

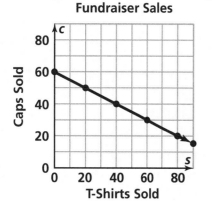

Fundraiser Sales

2. The ordered pairs can be connected and extended in a line. Any point that falls on the line will satisfy the equation.

C. 1. Answers will vary. Some possible answers are: $(6, 1), (7, 2), (8, 3), (9, 4), (5, 0), (0, -5)$; check graph for accuracy and other solution pairs.

2. Answers will vary. Some possible answers: $(0, 10), (1, 9), (2, 8), (4, 6), (10, 0)$; check graph for accuracy and other solution pairs.

3. Answers will vary. Some possible answers: $(0, 3), (\frac{3}{2}, 0), (1, 1), (2, -1), (3, -3), (-2, 7)$; check graph for accuracy and other solution pairs.

4. Answers will vary. Some possible answers are: $(0, -2), (1, -\frac{1}{2}), (\frac{4}{3}, 0), (2, 1), (4, 4), (-4, -8)$; check graph for accuracy.

D. The results suggest that for an equation that looks like $ax + by = c$, solutions will be represented by a straight line graph.

3.2 Connecting $y = mx + b$ and $ax + by = c$

Goals

- Connect the two forms of linear equations $y = mx + b$ and $ax + by = c$
- Practice working with algebraic equations

Launch 3.2

Use the Getting Ready to help launch the problem. In the last problem, students developed the idea that the graph of the solutions of the equation $ax + by = c$ is a straight line. They may already see a connection with equations of the form $y = mx + b$. However, students may have a sense that these feel different: in equations of the form $y = mx + b$, the functional relationship is explicit. y clearly depends on x. In equations of the form $ax + by = c$, the functional relationship is implicit. The variable y can still be said to depend on x, but not in such an obvious way; x might just as easily depend on y. This problem offers students a chance to make sure that indeed these two kinds of equations describe the same kind of graph.

You could launch this problem by asking what the graphs of $y = mx + b$ and $ax + by = c$ look like, and then asking the question from the text:

Suggested Question

- *Can linear equations such as* $ax + by = c$ *always be written in equivalent* $y = mx + b$ *form?*

You might work on Question A as a whole class so that the students see that the linear equation $ax + by = c$ can be written in $y = mx + b$ form and to model the kind of reasoning expected in the remaining problem parts. In Question A, students are asked to analyze someone else's reasoning. Then in Questions B through D they are to apply what they've observed to some new problems on their own.

Explore 3.2

As you circulate, listen to students' reasoning about why these algebraic manipulations work or do not work.

Going Further

Students needing an extra challenge might consider the inverse of the question in Question C.

- *If you have an equation in* $y = mx + b$ *form, how can you predict what* a, b *and* c *will be in the equivalent standard form?*

Because there are infinitely many equivalent equations in standard form, answers will vary. The simplest answer is that $a = m$, $b_{standard\ form} = -1$, and $c = -b_{slope\text{-}intercept\ form}$. This is based on the solution:

$$y = mx + b$$
$$-mx + y = b$$
$$mx - y = -b$$

Summarize 3.2

Ask students whether they now think that every equation of the form $ax + by = c$ can be written in an equivalent $y = mx + b$ form. Ask what it means that the two equations are equivalent. Focus on Question A for a moment, and ask if the students in the problem got an equation equivalent to the original. Invite students in the class to try to guess what the students in the problem were thinking.

Suggested Questions

- *Why would these students be confused?*
- *How did they get tripped up?*
- *If you were their teacher, how would you help them make sense of this algebra?*

One thing that may be confusing is that the parameter b shows up in both forms of the equation. As students begin to work on moving between the two equations, make sure that students understand that the b in $ax + by = c$ is not the y-intercept of the graph—it's just an unfortunate notational coincidence.

Finally, it is not the case that all equations of form $ax + by = c$ can be written in $y = mx + b$ form. In the special case where $b_{standard\ form} = 0$, we are left with $ax = c$, which describes a vertical line. Vertical lines have no slope, so there can be no slope-intercept form of the equation. For all other lines, though, we may write equations in both forms.

3.2 Connecting $y = mx + b$ and $ax + by = c$

Mathematical Goals

- Connect the two forms of linear equations $y = mx + b$ and $ax + by = c$
- Practice working with algebraic equations

Launch

Use the Getting Ready to help launch the problem. You could launch this problem by asking what the graphs of $y = mx + b$ and $ax + by = c$ look like, and then asking the question from the text:

- *Can linear equations such as* ax + by = c *always be written in equivalent* y = mx + b *form?*

You might work on Question A as a whole class so the students see that the linear equation $ax + by = c$ can be written in $y = mx + b$ form and to model the kind of reasoning expected in the remaining problem parts. In Question A, students are asked to analyze someone else's reasoning. Then in Questions B through D, they are to apply what they've observed to some new problems on their own.

Materials
- Transparencies 3.2A, 3.2B

Vocabulary
- linear equation in standard form

Explore

As you circulate, listen to students' reasoning about why these algebraic manipulations work or do not work.

Going Further: Students needing an extra challenge might consider the inverse of the question in Question C.

- *If you have an equation in* y = mx + b *form, how can you predict what* a, b, *and* c *will be in the equivalent standard form?*

Because there are infinitely many equivalent equations in standard form, answers will vary. The simplest answer is that $a = m$, $b_{\text{standard form}} = -1$, and $c = -b_{\text{slope-intercept form}}$.

Summarize

Ask students whether they now think that every equation of the form $ax + by = c$ can be written in an equivalent $y = mx + b$ form. Ask what it means that the two equations are equivalent. Focus on Question A for a moment, and ask if the students in the problem got an equation equivalent to the original.

- *Why would these students be confused?*
- *How did they get tripped up?*

Materials
- Student notebooks

Vocabulary
- slope-intercept form

ACE Assignment Guide for Problem 3.2

Differentiated Instruction
Solutions for All Learners

Core 15–27, 36–48
Other *Connections* 49, 50, *Extensions* 63, and unassigned choices from previous problems

Adapted For suggestions about adapting ACE exercises, see the CMP *Special Needs Handbook*.
Connecting to Prior Units 51, 57–62: *Moving Straight Ahead*; 52: *Say It With Symbols*; 53, 56: *Filling and Wrapping*; 54, 55: *Frogs, Fleas, and Painted Cubes*

Answers to Problem 3.2

A. 1. Jared: Yes; Jared used properties of equality: he subtracted $12x$ from both sides of the equation in the first step, which yielded an equivalent equation. Then he divided both sides of the equation by 3, continuing to maintain an equivalent equation. Dividing the right side $-12x + 9$ by 3 is the same as multiplying it by $\frac{1}{3}$, so $(-12x + 9) \div 3 = (-12x + 9)\frac{1}{3} = -4x + 3$.

Molly: No; she needed to divide both sides of the equation by 3. When she divided $9 - 12x$ by 3, she did not use the Distributive Property and forgot to divide $-12x$ by 3.

Ali: Yes; as in A, he maintained equivalent equations throughout his work. First he divided both sides of the equation by 3 and then subtracted $4x$ from either side.

Mia: No; $2.4x - 3$ is not equivalent to $3 - 4x$.

2. Two equations are equivalent if they have the same solutions.

B. 1. $y = x - 4$.

 2. $y = -2x + 9$.

 3. $y = -2x - 3$.

 4. $y = \frac{1}{2}x - 2$.

 5. $y = -x + 2.5$.

 6. $y = -\frac{1}{2}x + 60$.

C. The slope is $-\frac{a}{b}$. The y-intercept is $\frac{c}{b}$ and the x-intercept is $\frac{c}{a}$. Since $by = -ax + c$, $y = -\frac{a}{b}x + \frac{c}{b}$.

D. Answers will vary, as there are multiple equivalent forms for all equations in standard form. The answers given below use the smallest (in absolute value) whole-number coefficients.

 1. $3x + y = 5$

 2. $8x - 12y = -3$

 3. $x - 2y = -3$

 4. $4x - 2y = 1$

 5. $x - 4y = -12$

 6. $2x - y = 6$

3.3 Intersections of Lines

Goal

- Use graphical methods to solve systems of linear equations in standard form

Launch 3.3

Examine the information given in the introduction and highlight the overall question that students will solve by dealing with the specific questions in this problem. You might ask students to quickly guess what they think the numbers of adult and student memberships might have been, to record their guesses, and then to check to see if their guesses meet the given problem conditions.

While it is quite possible that some students will guess the correct answer (30 adult and 20 student memberships), it is unlikely that all students will have made that guess. Furthermore, since there are 51 different pairs to check [(0, 50), (1, 49), (2, 48), etc.], a guess-and-test strategy isn't particularly efficient, even in this fairly simple situation. Thus you can point out that the goal of work on this problem is to learn some systematic ways of solving problems like this one.

You might reinforce the idea that there are many possible pairs that satisfy one of the two equations by going over Question A together. Give students time to write the first equation, then ask,

Suggested Questions

- *Can you find two different solutions to this equation?*

Then have students write the equation in Question A, part (3).

- *Do the solutions in part 1 solve this equation also?*

Reinforce that this is the goal in this problem: finding common solutions to two equations.

Arrange students in groups of three or four to work on the problem.

Explore 3.3

You might want to have students focus on questions in Question A and have a whole-class discussion when most groups seem to have ideas about those questions, since accurate work on the rest of the problem depends on having accurate equations to work with.

Then have students work on the remainder of the problem.

Summarize 3.3

Go over the problem with the class. Make sure students know how to interpret the point of intersection from each part of Question B graphically, algebraically, and contextually. Graphically, this point is where the two lines meet. Algebraically, this is the coordinate (x, y) so that both equations are satisfied. In the context of the booster club membership sale, the intersection point of (30, 20) means that only a combination of 30 adult and 20 student memberships would lead to the reported $400 income.

Likely, students will have had little difficulty with these ideas, as they should be familiar from the grade 7 unit *Moving Straight Ahead* and other algebra units. In that unit, students solved a walking race problem that involved solving a system of linear equations, although the term system was not used.

Reinforce the concept of a point on a line being a solution to an equation (and a point not on a line not being a solution to the equation) by asking questions such as:

Suggested Questions

- *The point (10,60) is on one of the lines. Is it a solution to the system?* (No)

- *Why not?* (It is only on one of the lines. A solution to the system must be a solution to both equations; it must be on both lines.)

If students haven't answered Question C when it is time for a summary before class ends, you might assign this as homework.

3.3 Intersections of Lines

PACING $1\frac{1}{2}$ days

Mathematical Goal

• Use graphical methods to solve systems of linear equations in standard form

Launch

Examine the information given in the introduction and highlight the overall question that students will solve by dealing with the specific questions in this problem. You might ask students to quickly guess what they think the numbers of adult and student memberships might have been, to record their guesses, and then to check to see if their guesses meet the given problem conditions.

You might reinforce the idea that there are many possible pairs that satisfy one of the two equations by going over Question A together. Give students time to write the first equation, then ask,

• *Can you find two different solutions to this equation?*

Then have students write the equation in Question A, part (3) and ask,

• *Do the solutions in part 1 solve this equation also?*

Reinforce that this is the goal in this problem: finding common solutions to two equations.

Arrange students in groups of three or four to work on the problem.

Materials
• Transparency 3.3
• Labsheet 3.3 (1 per group)

Explore

You might want to have students focus on questions in Question A and have a whole-class discussion when most groups seem to have ideas about those questions, since accurate work on the rest of the problem depends on having accurate equations to work with.

Then have students work on the remainder of the problem.

Summarize

Go over the problem with the class. Make sure students know how to interpret the point of intersection from Question B graphically, algebraically, and contextually. Graphically, this point is where the two lines meet.

Reinforce the concept of a point on a line being a solution to an equation (and a point not on a line not being a solution to the equation) by asking questions such as:

• *The point (10, 60) is on one of the lines. Is it a solution to the system? Why not?*

If students haven't gotten to Question C when it is time for a summary before class ends, you might assign this as homework.

Materials
• Student notebooks

Vocabulary
• linear system

ACE Assignment Guide for Problem 3.3

Differentiated Instruction
Solutions for All Learners

Core 10–14
Other *Applications* 9, *Connections* 51–62, *Extensions* 64, 65 and unassigned choices from previous problems

Adapted For suggestions about adapting ACE exercises, see the CMP *Special Needs Handbook*.
Connecting to Prior Units 48, 50: *Moving Straight Ahead*; 50: *Say It With Symbols*

Answers to Problem 3.3

A. 1. $10x + 5y = 400$

   2. Answers will vary. (20, 40) and (10, 60) are 2 examples.

   3. $x + y = 50$; neither of the two examples above is also a solution for $x + y = 50$. (30, 20) is the only common solution.

B. 1. Graphs of the equations:
    $10x + 5y = 400$
      $x + y = 50$

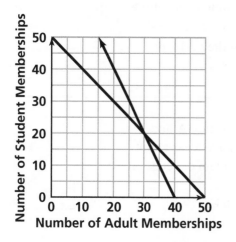

2. Since (30, 20) is on the line $10x + 5y = 400$, we know that 30 adult memberships and 20 student memberships will create a $400 income. Also, since (30, 20) is on the line $x + y = 50$, we know that we have a total of 50 memberships. The point (30, 20) satisfies both conditions.

3. No. The graph is the set of all points that are solutions to $10x + 5y = 400$. A point not on the graph line will not be a solution.

4. No; a common solution must be on both lines, and in particular, it must be a point of intersection of the two lines.

C. 1. (1, 3). Checking answer: $1 + 3 = 4$ and $1 - 3 = -2$.

   2. (1, −3). Checking answer: $2(1) + (-3) = -1$ and $1 - 2(-3) = 7$.

   3. (0, 3). Checking answer: $2(0) + 3 = 3$ and $-(0) + 2(3) = 6$.

Equations With Two or More Variables

You have done a lot of work with relationships involving two related variables. However, many real-world relationships involve three or more variables. For example, consider this situation:

The eighth-graders are selling T-shirts and caps to raise money for their end-of-year party. They earn a profit of $5 per shirt and $10 per cap.

This situation involves three variables: the *number of T-shirts sold*, the *number of caps sold,* and the *profit.* The profit for the fundraiser depends on the number of caps and the number of T-shirts sold.

Getting Ready for Problem 3.1

- What equation shows how the profit *p* is related to the number of shirts sold *s* and the number of caps sold *c*?

- Find the profit if the students sell
  - 30 shirts and 50 caps
  - 15 shirts and 10 caps
  - 12 shirts and 20 caps

- What do you think it means to *solve* an equation with three variables?

- What ideas do you have for finding solutions to the equation?

Investigation 3 Equations With Two or More Variables   **37**

Notes _____

_____
_____
_____

3.1 Many Ways to Reach a Goal

The equation relating *p, s,* and *c* represents every possible combination of T-shirts, caps, and profit values for the fundraiser. Suppose the class sets a profit goal of $P = \$600$. Finding combinations of T-shirt and cap sales that meet this goal requires solving an equation with only two variables, *s* and *c*.

Problem 3.1 Solving Equations With Two Variables

A. Find five pairs of numbers for shirt and cap sales that will allow the students to make a $600 profit exactly.

B. 1. Each answer for Question A can be expressed as an ordered pair (s, c). Plot these ordered pairs on a grid like the one below.

Fundraiser Sales

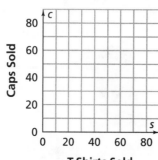

2. Is there a pattern in the points that suggests other solutions of the equation $600 = 5s + 10c$? Explain.

C. The equations in parts (1)–(4) are of the form $c = ax + by$ or $ax + by = c$. For each equation,

- find at least five solution pairs (x, y)
- plot the solutions
- find a pattern in the points and use the pattern to predict other solution pairs

1. $5 = x - y$ **2.** $10 = x + y$
3. $2x + y = 3$ **4.** $-3x + 2y = -4$

D. What does your work on Question C suggest about the graph of solutions for any equation of the form $ax + by = c$ or $c = ax + by$, where $a, b,$ and c are fixed numbers?

ACE Homework starts on page 42.

38   The Shapes of Algebra

Notes _____

_____

_____

_____

3.2 Connecting $y = mx + b$ and $ax + by = c$

There are two common forms of a linear equation.

- When the values of one variable depend on those of another, it is most natural to express the relationship as $y = mx + b$. Most of the linear equations you have seen have been in this *slope-intercept* form.

- When it is more natural to combine the values of two variables, the relationship can be expressed as $ax + by = c$. This is the *standard form* of a linear equation. The equations in Problem 3.1 were in standard form.

Getting Ready for Problem 3.2

It is easy to graph a linear equation of the form $y = mx + b$ on a calculator.

- Can you use a calculator to graph an equation of the form $ax + by = c$?
- Can you change an equation from $ax + by = c$ form to $y = mx + b$ form?
- How can rewriting the equation $600 = 5s + 10c$ (or $600 = 5x + 10y$) from Problem 3.1 in $y = mx + b$ form help you find solutions?

Problem 3.2 Connecting $y = mx + b$ and $ax + by = c$

A. Four students want to write $12x + 3y = 9$ in equivalent $y = mx + b$ form. Here are their explanations:

Jared

$12x + 3y = 9$
$\qquad 3y = -12x + 9 \quad (1)$
$\qquad y = -4x + 3 \quad (2)$

Molly

$12x + 3y = 9$
$\qquad 3y = 9 - 12x \quad (1)$
$\qquad y = 3 - 12x \quad (2)$

Ali

$12x + 3y = 9$
$\qquad 4x + y = 3 \quad (1)$
$\qquad y = -4x + 3 \quad (2)$

Mia

$12x + 3y = 9$
$\qquad 3y = 9 - 12x \quad (1)$
$\qquad y = 3 - 4x \quad (2)$
$\qquad y = 4x - 3 \quad (3)$

Investigation 3 Equations With Two or More Variables **39**

STUDENT PAGE

STUDENT PAGE

Notes _____

_____

_____

_____

(39) 68

1. Did each student get an equation equivalent to the original? If so, explain the reasoning for each step. If not, tell what errors the student made.

2. What does it mean for two equations to be equivalent?

B. Write each equation in $y = mx + b$ form.

1. $x - y = 4$ **2.** $2x + y = 9$ **3.** $8x + 4y = -12$

4. $12 = 3x - 6y$ **5.** $x + y = 2.5$ **6.** $600 = 5x + 10y$

C. Suppose you are given an equation in $ax + by = c$ form. How can you predict the slope, y-intercept, and x-intercept of its graph?

D. Write each equation in $ax + by = c$ form.

1. $y = 5 - 3x$ **2.** $y = \frac{2}{3}x + \frac{1}{4}$ **3.** $x = 2y - 3$

4. $2x = y + \frac{1}{2}$ **5.** $y - 2 = \frac{1}{4}x + 1$ **6.** $3y + 3 = 6x - 15$

ACE **Homework starts on page 42.**

3.3 Intersections of Lines

At a school band concert, Christopher and Celine sell memberships for the band's booster club. An adult membership costs $10, and a student membership costs $5.

At the end of the evening, the students had sold 50 memberships for a total of $400. The club president wants to know how many of the new members are adults and how many are students.

40 The Shapes of Algebra

Notes _____

_____

_____

_____

A. Let x stand for the number of $10 adult memberships and y for the number of $5 student memberships.

1. What equation relates x and y to the $400 income?

2. Give two solutions for your equation from part (1).

3. What equation relates x and y to the total of 50 new members? Are the solutions you found in part (2) also solutions of this equation?

B. 1. Graph the two equations from Question A on a single coordinate grid like the one at the right.

2. Estimate the coordinates of the point where the graphs intersect. Explain what the coordinates tell you about the numbers of adult and student memberships sold.

3. Consider the graph of the equation that relates x and y to the $400 income. Could a point that is *not* on this graph be a solution to the equation?

4. Could there be a common solution for both of your equations that is *not* shown on your graph?

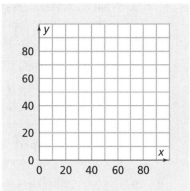

In Question A, you wrote a system of equations. One equation represents all (x, y) pairs that give a total income of $400, and the other represents all (x, y) pairs that give a total of 50 memberships. The coordinates of the intersection point satisfy both equations, or conditions. These coordinates are the *solution to the system*.

Many real-life problems can be represented by systems of equations. In Question C, you'll practice solving such systems graphically.

C. Use graphic methods to solve each system. In each case, substitute the solution values into the equations to see if your solution is exact or an estimate.

1. $x + y = 4$ and $x - y = -2$

2. $2x + y = -1$ and $x - 2y = 7$

3. $2x + y = 3$ and $-x + 2y = 6$

ACE Homework starts on page 42.

Notes _____

_____

_____

_____

Applications

1. For a fundraiser, students sell calendars for $3 each and posters for $2 each.

   a. What equation shows how the income *I* for the fundraiser depends on the number calendars *c* and posters *p* that are sold?

   b. What is the income if students sell 25 calendars and 18 posters?

   c. What is the income if students sell 12 calendars and 15 posters?

   d. What is the income if students sell 20 calendars and 12 posters?

   e. Find three combinations of calendar sales and poster sales that will give an income of exactly $100.

   f. Each answer in part (e) can be written as an ordered pair (c, p). Plot the ordered pairs on a coordinate grid.

   g. Use your graph to estimate three other (c, p) pairs that would meet the $100 goal.

2. Neema saves her quarters and dimes. She plans to exchange the coins for paper money when the total value equals $10.

   Homework Help Online
   PHSchool.com
   For: Help with Exercise 2
   Web Code: ape-7302

   a. How many coins does she need to make $10 if all the coins are quarters? If all the coins are dimes?

   b. What equation relates the number of quarters *x* and dimes *y* to the goal of $10?

   c. Use the answers from part (a) to help you draw a graph showing all solutions to the equation.

   d. Use the graph to find five combinations of dimes and quarters that will allow Neema to reach her goal.

42 The Shapes of Algebra

Notes _____

_____

_____

_____

3. Students in Eric's gym class must cover a distance of 1,600 meters by running or walking. Most students run part of the way and walk part of the way. Eric can run at an average speed of 200 meters per minute and walk at an average speed of 80 meters per minute.

  a. Suppose Eric runs for 4 minutes and walks for 8 minutes. How close is he to the 1,600-meter goal?

  b. Write an equation for the distance d Eric will cover if he runs for x minutes and walks for y minutes.

  c. Find three combinations of running and walking times for which Eric would cover 1,600 meters.

  d. Plot the ordered pairs for part (c) on a graph. Use the graph to estimate several other combinations of running and walking times for which Eric would cover 1,600 meters.

4. Kevin said that if you triple his age, the result will be 1 less than his mother's age.

  a. Which, if any, of these equations shows the relationship between Kevin's age x and his mother's age y? Choose all that are correct.

  $3x - y = 1$ $y - 3x = 1$ $3x + 1 = y$ $3x = 1 - y$

  b. Find three pairs of (x, y) values that satisfy the equation relating Kevin's age and his mother's age. Plot these ordered pairs, and draw the line that matches the pattern.

  c. Use the graph to estimate three other ordered pairs that satisfy the equation. Use the equation to check the estimates.

  d. Which (x, y) pairs seem to be reasonable for Kevin's age and his mother's age?

Find three pairs of (x, y) values that satisfy each equation. Plot those points and use the pattern to find two more solution pairs.

5. $6 = 3x - 2y$ (**Hint:** What is y if $x = 0$? What is x if $y = 0$?)

6. $10 = x + 2y$

7. $2x + y = 6$

8. $-3x + 4y = -4$

Notes _____

9. Tell which line at the right is the graph of each equation in parts (a)–(d). Explain.

a. $2x + 3y = 9$ **b.** $2x - 3y = 9$

c. $x - 3y = 6$ **d.** $3x + 2y = 6$

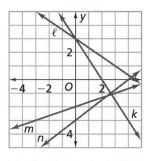

10. In Exercise 1, one equation relating the calendar and poster sales to the $600 goal is $3c + 2p = 600$. Suppose the company donating the calendars and posters said they would provide a total of 250 items.

a. What equation relates c and p to the 250 items donated?

b. Graph both equations on the same grid. Find the coordinates of the intersection point. Explain what these coordinates tell you about the fundraising situation.

11. In Exercise 2, one equation relating Neema's quarters and dimes to her goal of $10 (1,000 cents) is $25x + 10y = 1,000$. Suppose Neema collects 70 coins to reach her goal.

a. What equation relates x and y to the number of coins Neema collected?

b. Graph both equations on the same grid. Find the coordinates of the intersection point. Explain what these coordinates tell you about this situation.

12. In Exercise 3, one equation relating the times Eric spends running and walking to the goal of covering 1,600 meters is $200x + 80y = 1,600$. Suppose Eric runs and walks for a total of 12 minutes to reach his goal.

a. What equation relates x and y to Eric's total time?

b. Graph both equations on the same grid. Find the coordinates of the intersection point. Explain what these coordinates tell you about this situation.

44   The Shapes of Algebra

Notes _____

_____

_____

_____

13. In Exercise 4, one equation relating the ages of Kevin and his mother is $y - 3x = 1$. The sum of Kevin's age and his mother's age is 61 years.

   a. What equation relates Kevin's and his mother's ages to their total age?

   b. Graph both equations on the same grid. Find the coordinates of the intersection point. Explain what these coordinates tell you about the ages of Kevin and his mother.

14. Use graphing methods to solve each system of equations. [**Hint:** If you are using a graphing calculator, you can determine a good graphing window by first finding the x- and y-intercepts of each graph. For instance, find the x-intercept of $3x + 4y = 8$ by substituting 0 for y, and then find the y-intercept by substituting 0 for x.

   If $y = 0$, then $3x + 4(0) = 8$, so $x = \frac{8}{3}$. The x-intercept is $(\frac{8}{3}, 0)$.

   If $x = 0$, then $3(0) + 4y = 8$, so $y = 2$. The y-intercept is $(0, 2)$.]

   a. $x - y = -4$ and $x + y = 6$

   b. $-2x + y = 3$ and $x + 2y = -9$

   c. $-2x + y = 1$ and $4x - 2y = 6$

Write the equation in $ax + by = c$ form. Identify the x-intercept, y-intercept, and slope.

15. $y = 4x - 2$　　**16.** $y = -3x + 5$　　**17.** $y = x - 7$

18. $y = 5x + 3$　　**19.** $y = -8x - 12$　　**20.** $y = -9x + 5$

For Exercises 21–26, write the equation in $y = mx + b$ form. Identify the x-intercept, y-intercept, and slope.

21. $-2x - y = -5$　　**22.** $6x + 3y = -9$　　**23.** $x - y = 4$

24. $3x + 4y = 12$　　**25.** $-7x + 2y = -16$　　**26.** $x - 5y = 55$

27. Look back over your work for Exercises 15–26. Look for patterns relating the standard form of the equation, $ax + by = c$, to the x-intercept, y-intercept, and slope.

   a. Write a general formula for calculating the x-intercept from the values of a, b, and c.

   b. Write a general formula for calculating the y-intercept from the values of a, b, and c.

   c. Write a general formula for calculating the slope from the values of a, b, and c.

Notes _____

_____

_____

_____

Connections

Solve the inequality and graph the solution on a number line.

28. $x + 3 < 5$ **29.** $x - 12 > -4$

30. $14 + x \le -2$ **31.** $2x + 7 \ge -3$

32. $7x + 3 \le -17 + 2x$ **33.** $-3 - 4x \ge 5x + 24$

34. $2x - 4 + 7x < -6x + 41$ **35.** $12x - 3 + 5 - 4x > 24 - 2x + 8$

Write an equation of a line parallel to the given line.

36. $y = 4x + 6$ **37.** $-6x + y = 3$ **38.** $x + y = 9$

39. $x + 4y = -20$ **40.** $y = -\frac{3}{4}x - 2$ **41.** $7x + y = -12$

For Exercises 42–47, write an equation of a line perpendicular to the given line.

42. $y = -4x + 2$ **43.** $y = -\frac{2}{3}x - 7$ **44.** $y = 6x + 12$

45. $-2x + y = -1$ **46.** $x - 4y = 20$ **47.** $2x + 3y = 8$

48. Tell whether each ordered pair is a solution of $3x - 5y = 15$. Show how you know.

    a. $(-2, -4)$ **b.** $(0, -3)$ **c.** $(-10, 9)$

    d. $(-5, -6)$ **e.** $(-10, -9)$ **f.** $(-4, -5.4)$

For: Multiple-Choice Skills Practice
Web Code: apa-7354

49. The angle measures of the triangle below are $x, y,$ and z.

    a. What equation shows how z depends on x and y?

    b. Find five combinations of values for x and y for which the value of z is 40.

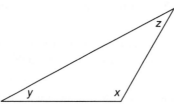

STUDENT PAGE

Notes _____

_____

_____

_____

50. **Multiple Choice** Suppose k, m, and n are numbers and $k = m + n$. Which of the following statements must be true?

   A. $k - m = n$ **B.** $m - k = n$

   C. $2k = 2m + n$ **D.** $-n = k + m$

51. **Multiple Choice** Which equation is equivalent to $3x + 5y = 15$?

   F. $3x = 5y + 15$ **G.** $x = -5y + 5$

   H. $y = 0.6x + 3$ **J.** $y = -0.6x + 3$

52. Suppose you are given the linear equation $ax + by = c$.

   a. What is the slope of every line parallel to this line?

   b. What is the slope of every line perpendicular to this line?

53. You will need two sheets of grid paper and two different cans with paper labels (for example, tuna and soup cans). On grid paper, trace the top and bottom of each can. Cut these out. Now carefully remove the labels and trace these on grid paper.

   a. Estimate and compare the surface areas of the cans (label + top + bottom or $A = \ell w + 2\pi r^2$).

   b. After Joel removes his two labels, he notices that the labels are the exact same size and shape. Explain how this can happen.

Notes _____

_____

_____

_____

54. Multiple Choice Which values are solutions of the quadratic equation $x^2 + 8x - 33 = 0$?

    A. $x = -11$ and $x = -3$ **B.** $x = 11$ and $x = -3$

    C. $x = -11$ and $x = 3$ **D.** $x = 11$ and $x = 3$

55. Use the graph of $y = x^2 + 8x - 33$ to find the solution of each inequality.

    a. $x^2 + 8x - 33 > 0$ **b.** $x^2 + 8x - 33 < 0$

56. a. What shape will this net make if it is cut out and folded?

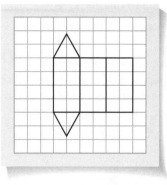

    b. Find the surface area of the shape.

    c. Find the volume of the shape.

57. Tell whether each line has a slope of $-\frac{1}{2}$.

    a. $y = \frac{-1}{-2}x + 3$ **b.** $y = \frac{-1}{2}x + 3$

    c. $y = \frac{1}{-2}x + 3$ **d.** $y = -\frac{1}{2}x + 3$

Without graphing, decide whether the lines are parallel, perpendicular, or neither.

58. $3x + 6y = 12$ and $y = 10 + \frac{-1}{2}x$

59. $y = -x + 5$ and $y = x + 5$

60. $y = 2 - 5x$ and $y = -5x + 2$

61. $y = -3 + 5x$ and $y = \frac{-x}{5} + 3$

62. $10x + 5y = 20$ and $y = 10x + 20$

Notes _____

_____

_____

_____

STUDENT PAGE

Extensions

63. Jasmine wants to run a marathon. She knows she will have to walk some of the 26.2 miles, but she wants to finish in 5 hours. She plans to run 10-minute miles and walk 15-minute miles.

Let x stand for the number of minutes Jasmine runs. Let y stand for the number of minutes she walks.

a. What equation relates x and y to the goal of completing the race in 5 hours?

b. What equation relates x and y to the goal of covering 26.2 miles?

c. For each equation, find several ordered-pair solutions (x, y). Then, plot the points with those coordinates and use the pattern to draw a graph of the equation. Graph both equations on the same axes.

d. Use the graphs to estimate the combination of running and walking times that will allow Jasmine to complete the marathon in exactly 5 hours.

e. Suppose Jasmine decides she wants to finish the marathon in less than 5 hours. Find five combinations of running and walking times that give a total time less than 5 hours.

f. Express the condition that the total running and walking times must be less than 5 hours as an inequality.

g. Make a graph of all the solutions of the inequality.

h. Graph the linear equation from part (b) on the same axes as the inequality. Explain how the result shows Jasmine's options for running and walking times if she wants to finish the marathon in 5 hours or less.

Notes _____

_____

_____

_____

64. a. Find coordinates of the midpoints of the sides of this triangle.

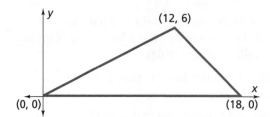

b. A segment from one vertex of a triangle to the midpoint of the opposite side is called a *median*. Find equations of the three medians of this triangle.

c. Use algebraic methods to find the coordinates of the point(s) where the median from the vertex $(12, 6)$ intersects the other medians.

d. The medians of any triangle intersect at a single point called the *centroid*. The centroid divides each median into two pieces that are related. Study the coordinates of the vertices, midpoints, and centroid of the triangle above. What is the special way in which the centroid splits each median?

e. Use the coordinates of the centroid and the vertices to calculate the lengths of the two segments that make up each median. Explain how the results confirm your answer to part (d) or how they suggest a revision of your original idea.

65. Your exploration in Exercise 64 focused on a single triangle. To test the patterns you observed, repeat the analysis from those problems with these other triangles.

a. A triangle with vertices $(0, 0), (12, 0)$ and $(-6, 6)$

b. A triangle with vertices $(0, 0), (12, 0)$ and $(4, 12)$

50   The Shapes of Algebra

Notes _____

_____

_____

_____

Mathematical Reflections 3

In this investigation, you used coordinate graphs to display solutions of linear equations of the form $ax + by = c$ and to find solutions of systems of linear equations. These questions will help you summarize what you have learned.

Think about your answers to these questions. Discuss your ideas with other students and your teacher. Then write a summary of your findings in your notebook.

Give specific examples to illustrate your answers to Questions 1–3.

1. What pattern will result from plotting all points (x, y) that satisfy an equation in the form $ax + by = c$?

2. How can you use a graph to find values of x and y that satisfy systems of two linear equations in the form $ax + by = c$?

3. How can you change linear equations of the form $ax + by = c$ to $y = mx + b$ form and vice versa?

Notes _____

_____

_____

_____

Investigation

ACE Assignment Choices

Differentiated Instruction
Solutions for All Learners

Problem 3.1

Core 1–8, 28–35
Other Unassigned choices from previous problems

Problem 3.2

Core 15–27, 36–48
Other 49, 50, 63, and unassigned choices from previous problems

Problem 3.3

Core 10–14
Other 9, 51–62, 64, 65 and unassigned choices from previous problems

Adapted For suggestions about adapting Exercise 2 and other ACE exercises, see the CMP *Special Needs Handbook.*
Connecting to Prior Units 36–48, 50–52, 57–62: *Moving Striaght Ahead*; 50–52: *Say It With Symbols*; 53, 56: *Filling and Wrapping*; 54, 55: *Frogs, Fleas, and Painted Cubes*

Applications

1. **a.** $I = 3c + 2p$

   b. $3(25) + 2(18) = 111$

   c. $3(12) + 2(15) = 66$

   d. $3(20) + 2(12) = 84$

   e. Some possible pairs include $(0, 50)$, $(10, 35)$, $(20, 20)$, $(30, 5)$

   f. The graphs may look something like the ones above at the right.

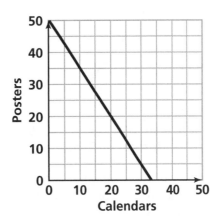

Note: The scales can be determined by finding the points where the line intercepts the horizontal and vertical axes. Since there is no dependence relationship between the posters and the calendars, it does not matter which variable is on the horizontal axis and which is on the vertical axis. The intercepts for the graph on the left are $(33.3, 0)$ and $(0, 50)$ and the graph the right $(0, 33.3)$ and $(50, 0)$.

g. Estimates of other pairs might include $(4, 44)$, $(16, 26)$, $(26, 11)$, etc. for the graph on the left and $(44, 4)$, $(26, 16)$, $(11, 26)$, etc. for the graph on the right. Note to the teacher: The two graphs are mirror images of each other after a reflection in line $y = x$. So the coordinates of the graph on the left can be used to find the coordinates for the graph on the right by applying the transformation $(x, y) \rightarrow (y, x)$.

2. a. 40 quarters; 100 dimes

b. $0.25x + 0.10y = 10$; where x is the number of quarters and y is the number of dimes.

c.

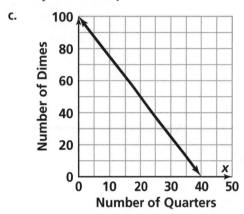

d. Only positive whole number pairs which you can read from the graph will work. They include $(8, 80)$, $(16, 60)$, $(24, 40)$, $(32, 20)$, etc.

3. a. 160 m; $200(4) + 80(8) = 1{,}440$, so Eric could get $1{,}600 - 1{,}440 = 160$m from the goal.

b. $200x + 80y = d$

c. $200x + 80y = 1{,}600$ in case $(4, 10)$, $(0, 20)$, $(8, 0)$, etc.

d.

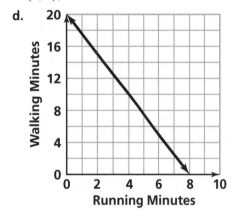

4. a. $y - 3x = 1$ and $3x + 1 = y$ are correct.

b. Possible ordered pairs include $(0,1)$, $(5, 16)$, $(10, 31)$, $(15, 46)$, etc.

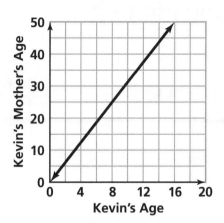

c. Only positive whole number ordered pairs will work including $(2, 7)$, $(4, 13)$, $(6, 19)$, $(8, 25)$, etc.

d. Reasonable solutions are $(10, 31)$ and $(15, 46)$.

5. $6 = 3x - 2y$ has solutions $(0, -3)$, $(2, 0)$, and $(4, 3)$ among many others, including points such as $(1, -1.5)$, $(3, 1.5)$, $(5, 4.5)$, and $(-1, -4.5)$. The graph is shown below.

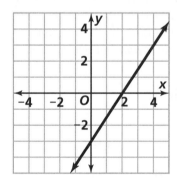

6. $10 = x + 2y$ has solutions $(0, 5)$, $(4, 3)$, $(-2, 6)$, $(6, 2)$, and many others, including points such as $(2, 4)$, $(8, 1)$, $(1, 4.5)$, $(3, 3.5)$, $(5, 2.5)$, etc.

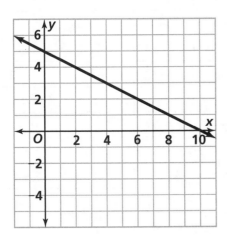

7. $2x + y = 6$ includes solutions $(0, 6)$, $(1, 4)$, $(3, 0)$, $(5, -4)$, and many others, including points such as $(2, 2)$, $(4, -2)$, $(1.5, 3)$, etc.

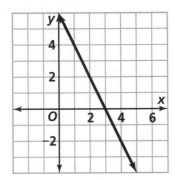

8. $-3x + 4y = -4$ has solutions including $(0, -1)$, $\left(\frac{4}{3}, 0\right)$, $(4, 2)$, and many others, such as points $(-4, -4)$, $(-2, -2.5)$, $(2, 0.5)$, $(6, 3.5)$, etc.

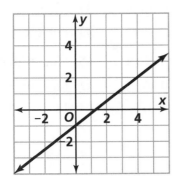

9. Students may verify their claims by comparing slopes and y-intercepts.

  a. $2x + 3y = 9$ is line l

  b. $2x - 3y = 9$ is line n

  c. $x - 3y = 6$ is line m

  d. $3x + 2y = 6$ is line k

10. a. $c + p = 250$

  b. The graphs intersect at $(100, 150)$, meaning that 100 calendars and 150 posters will meet the limit of the donor and also the goal of earning \$600 for the fund-raiser.

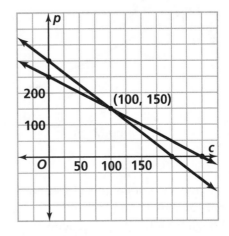

11. a. $x + y = 70$

  b. The graphs intersect at $(20, 50)$, meaning that 20 quarters and 50 dimes will meet the condition of 70 coins and value of 1,000 cents.

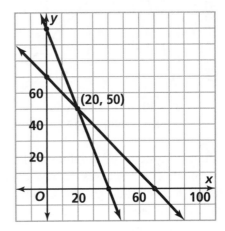

12. a. $x + y = 12$

b. The intersection point is $(5\frac{1}{3}, 6\frac{2}{3})$, though from the graph students might only estimate $(5, 7)$ or perhaps $(5.5, 6.5)$. This means that if one runs for a bit more than 5 minutes and walks for a bit less than 7 minutes at the predicted speeds, the goal of 1,600 meters in 12 minutes should be reached.

13. a. $x + y = 61$

b. The intersection point is $(15, 46)$ meaning that Kevin is 15 and his mother is 46, though from the graph students might only be able to estimate $(15, 45)$.

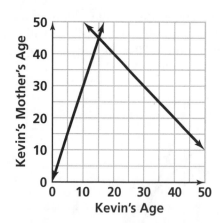

14. Solutions to systems by graphing will only be approximate in many cases. Always expect students to check their graphic estimates by substitution to see if they are accurate.

a. Solution is $(1, 5)$

b. Solution is $(-3, -3)$

c. Lines are parallel, meaning that there is no common solution to the equations.

	Equation	x-intercept	y-intercept	Slope
15.	$-4x + y = -2$	$\frac{1}{2}$	-2	4
16.	$3x + y = 5$	$\frac{5}{3}$	5	-3
17.	$-x + y = -7$	7	-7	1
18.	$-5x + y = 3$	$-\frac{3}{5}$	3	5
19.	$8x + y = -12$	$-\frac{3}{2}$	-12	-8
20.	$9x + y = 5$	$\frac{5}{9}$	5	-9
21.	$y = -2x + 5$	$\frac{5}{2}$	5	-2
22.	$y = -2x - 3$	$-\frac{3}{2}$	-3	-2
23.	$y = x - 4$	4	-4	1
24.	$y = (-\frac{3}{4})x + 3$	4	3	$-\frac{3}{4}$
25.	$y = (\frac{7}{2})x - 8$	$\frac{16}{7}$	-8	$\frac{7}{2}$
26.	$y = 0.2x - 11$	55	-11	0.2

27. a. x-intercept is always $(\frac{c}{a}, 0)$ because $ax + b(0) = c$ has that solution.

b. y-intercept is always $(0, \frac{c}{b})$ because $a(0) + by = c$ has that solution.

c. Slope is always $-\frac{a}{b}$ because $ax + by = c$ is equivalent to $by = -ax + c$ and then to $y = (-\frac{a}{b})x + (\frac{c}{b})$.

Connections

28–35. Check students' graphs.

28. $x < 2$ **29.** $x > 8$ **30.** $x \leq -16$ **31.** $x \geq -5$

32. $x \leq -4$ **33.** $x \leq -3$ **34.** $x < 3$ **35.** $x > 3$

36. Lines with slope 4 **37.** Lines with slope 6

38. Lines with slope -1 **39.** Lines with slope $-\frac{1}{4}$

40. Lines with slope $-\frac{3}{4}$ **41.** Lines with slope -7

42. Lines with slope $\frac{1}{4}$ **43.** Lines with slope $\frac{3}{2}$

44. Lines with slope $-\frac{1}{6}$ **45.** Lines with slope $-\frac{1}{2}$

46. Lines with slope -4 **47.** Lines with slope $\frac{3}{2}$

48. a. No: $3(-2) - 5(-4) = 14$

b. Yes **c.** No

d. Yes **e.** Yes

f. Yes

49. a. $z = 180 - (x + y)$ or $z = 180 - x - y$ or
$x + y + z = 180$.

b. $40 = 180 - (x + y)$ is satisfied by (x, y)
like $(120, 20)$, $(100, 40)$, $(40, 100)$, and so on.

50. A   **51.** J

52. a. Slopes of parallel lines will be $-\frac{a}{b}$
where $b \neq 0$.

b. Slopes of perpendicular lines will be $\frac{b}{a}$
where $a \neq 0$.

53. a. Answers will vary. Students may be quite
inaccurate if they are counting grid squares
to get the area.

b. The labels are rectangles. In each case, one
dimension of the rectangle must wrap
around the can, so this dimension must
match the circumference of the circular
base. The other dimension of the
rectangular label must match the height of
the can. If we switch the ℓ and w, then the
labels are still the same size and shape.
Note: Students investigated this idea in
Filling and Wrapping when they used a
sheet of $8.5" \times 11"$ paper to make two
different cylinders, one $8.5"$ high and the
other $11"$ high.

54. C

55. a. $x < -11$ or $x > 3$

b. $-11 < x < 3$

56. a. The figure will be a right prism with
triangular bases.

b. The surface area will be about 28 grid
squares. (For exact: $24 + 2\sqrt{3}$ or 27.5 grid
squares.)

c. The volume will be the area of the base
times the height or about $2 \times 4 = 8$ cubic
units. (Exact: $\sqrt{3} \times 4 \approx 6.9$ cubic units)

57. b, c, and d all have slope $-\frac{1}{2}$.

58. Parallel; Their slopes are both $-\frac{1}{2}$. The
equations in $y = mx + b$ form are
$y = -\frac{1}{2}x + 2$ and $y = -\frac{1}{2}x + 10$.

59. Perpendicular; their slopes are negative
reciprocals since the reciprocal of 1 is itself.

60. Neither, they are the same line.

61. Perpendicular; the slope of the equation
$y = -3 + 5x$ is 5 and the slope of
$y = -\frac{x}{5} + 3$ is $-\frac{1}{5}$. Since 5 and $-\frac{1}{5}$ are negative
reciprocals the lines are perpendicular.

62. Neither; the slope of the line represented by
the equation $10x + 5y = 20$ is -2, and the
slope for the second line is 10.

Extensions

63. a. $\frac{x}{60} + \frac{y}{60} = 5$ **b.** $\frac{x}{10} + \frac{y}{15} = 26.2$

c. Solutions to the equation in part (a):
$(0, 300)$, $(300, 0)$, $(150, 150)$, etc.

Solutions to the equation in part (b):
$(0, 393)$, $(262, 0)$, $(100, 243)$, $(162, 150)$.

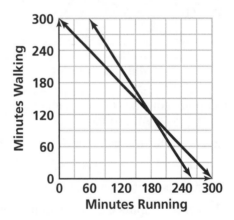

d. The graph suggests a combination of
running and walking times in the vicinity of
180 minutes running and 120 minutes
walking. The exact solution is $(186, 114)$, so
the graph gives a good estimate.
$\frac{186}{10} + \frac{114}{15} = 26.2$

e. Combinations of times less than 5 hours:
$(100, 199)$, $(199, 100)$, $(100, 150)$, etc.

f. $x + y < 300$ or $\frac{x}{60} + \frac{y}{60} < 5$

g. The graph of the inequality in (b) will be a
region to the left and below the graph of
the equation $x + y = 300$.

h. When the distance equation is graphed on the region showing times less than 5 hours, it indicates a segment of the graph where coordinates will represent distance of 26.2 miles and time less than or equal to 5 hours. Note that this solution is only the intersection of the line and the shaded region. We have circled the indicated part on the graph.

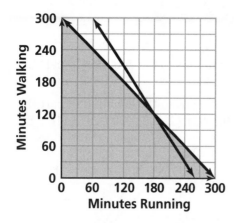

64. a. Midpoints of sides of the triangle are $(6, 3)$, $(15, 3)$, and $(9, 0)$.

b. Equations for the medians are: $y = 0.2x$; $y = 2x - 18$; $y = -(\frac{1}{4})x + 4.5$.

c. The medians intersect at $(10, 2)$.

d. The centroid splits each median into two segments that are in the ratio 2 to 1.

e. Segment lengths for the median from $(0, 0)$ to $(15, 3)$ are about 10.2 and 5.1. Segment lengths for the median from $(12, 6)$ to $(9, 0)$ are about 4.48 and 2.24. Segment lengths for the median from $(18, 0)$ to $(6, 3)$ are about 8.24 and 4.12. These results confirm the answers from part (d).

65. a. Midpoints of sides of the triangle are $(3, 3)$, $(-3, 3)$, and $(6, 0)$. Equations for the medians are: $y = x$; $y = -0.5x + 3$; $y = -0.2x + 2.4$. The medians intersect at $(2, 2)$. Segment lengths for the median from $(0, 0)$ to $(3, 3)$ are $2\sqrt{2}$ and $\sqrt{2}$. Segment lengths for the median from $(-6, 6)$ to $(6, 0)$ are $4\sqrt{5}$ and $2\sqrt{5}$. Segment lengths for the median from $(12, 0)$ to $(-3, 3)$ are $2\sqrt{26}$ and $\sqrt{26}$.

b. Midpoints of sides of the triangle are $(8, 6)$, $(2, 6)$, and $(6, 0)$. Equations for the medians are: $y = 0.75x$; $y = -6x + 36$; $y = -0.6x + 7.2$. The medians intersect at $(\frac{16}{3}, 4)$. Segment lengths for the median from $(0, 0)$ to $(8, 6)$ are $\frac{20}{3}$ and $\frac{10}{3}$. Segment lengths for the median from $(12, 0)$ to $(2, 6)$ are $\frac{4\sqrt{34}}{3}$ and $\frac{2\sqrt{34}}{3}$. Segment lengths for the median from $(4, 12)$ to $(6, 0)$ are $\frac{4\sqrt{10}}{3}$ and $\frac{2\sqrt{10}}{3}$.

Possible Answers to Mathematical Reflections

1. You will graph a straight line.

2. If you graph the lines associated with each equation, they may intersect at a point. The coordinates of the point of intersection will satisfy each equation in the system. You need to rewrite the equations in slope-intercept form if you want to use your calculator to make the graphs.

3. To get from $ax + by = c$ to $y = mx + b$ form, you need to solve for y. You could write: $by = c - ax$, and then $y = \frac{c}{b} - (\frac{a}{b})x$, and then: $y = (-\frac{a}{b})x + \frac{c}{b}$. This equation has the form $y = mx + k$, where $m = -\frac{a}{b}$ and $k = \frac{c}{b}$. To get from $y = mx + b$ to $ax + by = c$ is even easier. You just need to write: $-mx + y = b$.

Reminder: There is a strong potential for notational confusion because the letter b stands for different quantities in the two equation forms.

Investigation 4

Solving Systems of Linear Equations Symbolically

Mathematical and Problem-Solving Goals

- Review solving systems of linear equations in the form $y = m_1x + b_1$ and $y = m_2x + b_2$
- Develop and use the strategy for solving systems of linear equations in the form

$$\begin{cases} ax + by = c \\ dx + ey = f \end{cases}$$

  by solving both equations for y in terms of x (or for x in terms of y if that is more convenient)
- Develop and use the strategy for solving systems of linear equations by substitution
- Develop and use the strategy for solving systems of linear equations by forming linear combinations
- Choose strategically among the three algebraic methods which to use for a particular system of linear equations

Work in Investigation 3 has laid the conceptual groundwork for understanding what it means to solve a system of linear equations. The aim of this investigation is to develop understanding and skill in use of several standard strategies for finding the solutions by algebraic reasoning.

Summary of Problems

Problem 4.1   The $y = mx + b$ Case

Addresses the familiar and simplest case in which both equations express y as a function of x and the solution results from setting those two expressions equal to each other and solving the single variable equation.

Problem 4.2   The $ax + by = c$ Case

Addresses the cases of linear systems in which it is relatively easy to transform each of the given equations (in the form $ax + by = c$) into "$y = \ldots$" or "$x = \ldots$" form and then proceed as in Problem 4.1.

Problem 4.3   Solving Systems of Linear Equations by Substitution

Addresses the cases in which one of the equations can be transformed into "$y = \ldots$" or "$x = \ldots$" and the result substituted into the other equation to yield an equation in one variable.

Problem 4.4   Solving Systems of Linear Equations by Combination

Addresses the standard linear combinations method in which multiples of one or both given equations are combined by addition or subtraction in a way that again eliminates one of the unknowns.

	Suggested Pacing	Materials for Students	Materials for Teachers	ACE Assignments
All	$5\frac{1}{2}$ days	graph paper	Poster paper (optional)	
4.1	1 day		Transparencies 4.1A, 4.1B	1–7, 27–37, 61
4.2	$1\frac{1}{2}$ days		Transparency 4.2	8–14, 38–46, 62
4.3	1 day		Transparency 4.3A, 4.3B	15–20, 47–50, 63
4.4	$1\frac{1}{2}$ days		Transparency 4.4	21–26, 51–60, 64–67
MR	$\frac{1}{2}$ day			

The $y = mx + b$ Case

Goal

- Review solving equations of the form $m_1x + b_1 = m_2x + b_2$

This should be relatively familiar mathematics from *Moving Straight Ahead* and *Say It With Symbols*, so you can probably move quickly through this problem.

Launch 4.1

Refer to the diagram on page 52 of the student edtion to get students started with this problem.

Suggested Questions

- *The diagram seems to show many potential mid-air collisions of planes. Why do you suppose that such disasters almost never occur?* (The planes reach the intersection points of the flight planes at different altitudes. The planes travel at different times so they reach the intersection points at different times.)

- *What information about flight paths and plans is not shown by the diagram?* (The altitudes the planes are traveling along their flight plan and how their altitude does or does not change. The speeds the planes are traveling and the time the planes are traveling along the paths.)

List the flight path equations on the board. Consider the Getting Ready questions. Explain that:

- *You are going to find the intersection points for flight plans. For example, for the flight plans of WC 19 and AA 29, you need to find a point (x, y) so that x and y values of this point satisfy both equations in the system:*

$$\begin{cases} y = 0.3x - 2 \\ y = 1.5x - 0.4 \end{cases}$$

- *What does it mean to satisfy both equations in the system?*

- *How would you find the solution?*

Discuss Jeff's solution with your students. Use this conversation to assess what kinds of assistance they will need as they work through the parts of the problem.

Tell students that in this investigation they will practice solving systems of linear equations symbolically. This is a helpful tool when you need to know the precise location of intersections of lines and not just estimates from a graph.

Explore 4.1

Have students find the intersection points for their flight plans using symbolic methods.

For students who are having difficulty remembering how to solve systems algebraically, help them realize that the intersection point will have coordinates that satisfy both equations.

Suggested Questions

- *If we want to find values of* x *and* y *that satisfy both equations, what must be true of* $0.3x - 2$ *and* $1.5x - 0.4$, *if you are solving this system?*

$$\begin{cases} y = 0.3x - 2 \\ y = 1.5x - 0.4 \end{cases}$$

We are looking for the one point (x_1, y_1) that satisfies both equations. That is, when we evaluate the expressions on the right-hand side of each equation at x_1, we get the same value. This means that $0.3x_1 - 2 = 1.5x_1 - 0.4$.

Have students check that the resulting y-value (y_1) will be the same, regardless of which equation is used.

- *If you substitute the value of* x *into both equations, what do you get?*

While this might be a bit surprising at first, it happens because of the way x was determined—we look for a value of x that produces the same values when substituted into either expression for y.

Going Further

As an extra challenge, ask:

- *Find the intersection points for these flights:*
  WC 19 and OS 314
  (discussion of solution below)

(WC 19 and OS 314 are parallel and so have no common solution.) Have students who work on this try to solve one of the other systems first and compare it to their problem. If they get down to an equation like: $0x = 3$, ask them if there is any x that satisfies this equation. Some students may get down to an equation such as $0 = 3$. Ask them if this makes sense. You may want to ask them about a previous step in their equation-solving process before the variable, x, dropped out. For example, when solving the equation $0.3x + 2 = 0.3x + 5$, students may subtract five from both sides to get that $0.3x - 3 = 0.3x$. This equation does not have a solution because $0.3x$ is some number and a number minus three can never equal itself. Thus there is no value for x that will give the same y-value for both expressions in the system, so there is no intersection point. Another way you can have students begin to reason about this problem is to think about the graphical picture of these two systems shown in the Student Edition.)

- *If you look at the graph of the lines, what might you expect the intersection to be?* (The lines are parallel because they have the same slope. Therefore, the lines will not have an intersection point.)

Suggested Questions

To help students struggling at starting Question B, ask:

- *What was your first step when you solved the system in Question A?*
- *What would the equation look like if you performed that first step on the general system*

$$\begin{cases} y = ax + b \\ y = cx + d \end{cases}$$

- *If you solved this general system for x, what would you get?*

When most students have attempted Question B, move on to the summary. Question B is a challenging part of this problem. It can be discussed as a whole class in the summary.

Summarize 4.1

Have groups display their work and explain their thinking for Question A.

Suggested Questions

- *How can we check whether a point is an intersection point?* (Substitute the x- and y-coordinates of the point into both equations and make sure the point satisfies both equations.)
- *How many intersection points can we have for any two flight plans?* (Since the flight plans are linear, there are only three possibilities: 0 intersection points, 1 intersection point, and infinitely many intersection points.)

When there are zero intersection points, the lines are parallel.

The case in which there are infinitely many intersection points is the case in which the two flight plans are equivalent, such as $2y = 4x + 6$ and $y = 2x + 3$. An example of such a system was not given in the problem. However, you may want to pose the system to your students if they offer only 0 and 1 as possible numbers of intersection points. This case will be discussed in Problem 4.3.

Suggested Questions

- *Are there any flight plan lines that do not intersect each other? How do you know?* (Yes. WC 19 and OS 314 are parallel flight plans, which can be seen from the graph and from the equations since they have the same slope of 0.3.)
- *What happens when you solve this system algebraically? Why do you think that happens?* (The variable is eliminated and you get an equation that is never true, like $0 = 3$ or $0 = -3$. This happens because there is no intersection point, so there is no value for x, which when substituted into both equations, gives the same y-value.)

This case will also be discussed further in Problem 4.3.

Then check the match between the groups' algebraically calculated results and the location of intersection points on the flight plan diagram in the Student Edition.

Suggested Questions

- *Do your calculated results seem to match the approximate intersection points on the graph?*

If groups obtained different answers for the intersection points of two particular flight plans ask students:

- *Can both groups be correct?*

- *How would you decide which one is correct?* (Students may suggest estimating from the graph in the Student Edition which intersection point seems more reasonable or checking the points from each group in both equations in the system.)

Discuss Question B as a whole group:

Let's look at an example to help us as we think about the general form. Let's take OS 314 and FA 12.

Write the two systems on the board along with the equation found by setting the expressions of y equal:

$$\begin{cases} y = 0.3x + 5 \\ y = 0.4x + 9.5 \\ 0.3x + 5 = 0.4x + 9.5 \end{cases} \qquad \begin{cases} y = ax + b \\ y = cx + d \\ ax + b = cx + d \end{cases}$$

- *What is the first thing you would do to solve $0.3x + 5 = -0.4x + 9.5$?*

For each step in solving the system on the left, write the parallel step for the general system on the right. Students may decide to perform operations in a different order. For example, above right, 5 is subtracted from both sides first. However 9.5 could have been subtracted first, $0.3x$ could have been subtracted first or $0.4x$

added to both sides first. Make sure the general equation models the steps suggested by students for solving the equation $0.3x + 5 = -0.4x + 9.5$.

$$0.3x + 5 = -0.4x + 9.5$$
$$0.3x = -0.4x + 9.5 - 5$$
$$0.3x + 0.4x = 4.5$$
$$(0.3 + 0.4)x = 4.5$$
$$x = \frac{4.5}{0.7} \approx 6.43$$

$$ax + b = cx + d$$
$$ax = cx + d - b$$
$$ax - cx = d - b$$
$$(a - c)x = d - b$$
$$x = \frac{d - b}{a - c}$$

Continue modeling the general equation on the right after student suggestions for solving the equation on the left.

Students should not memorize these general solutions, $x = \frac{d - b}{a - c}$. Rather, it is the general process that should be emphasized.

Going Further You may want to discuss how this general analysis reveals the fact that when the two lines have the same slope, $a = c$ in the system and the formula for x is undefined since $x = \frac{d - b}{0}$.

That is, when the two lines are parallel, there is either no solution ($d \neq b$) or infinitely many solutions ($d = b$).

In the process of solving systems in which the lines are parallel or are the same line, the algebraic maneuvers will lead to equations such as $0 = k$ where k is some non-zero number (no solutions) or $0 = 0$ (infinitely many solutions).

Ask students for their suggestions about Question C.

The $y = mx + b$ Case

Mathematical Goal

- Review student skills in solving equations of the form
  $m_1x + b_1 = m_2x + b_2$

Launch

Refer to the diagram on page 52 to get students started with this problem.

- *The diagram seems to show many potential mid-air collisions of planes. Why do you suppose that such disasters almost never occur?*

- *What information about flight paths and plans is not shown by the diagram?*

List the flight path equations on the board. Consider the Getting Ready questions. Explain that:

- *You are going to find the intersection points for flight plans. For example, for the flight plans of WC 19 and AA 29, you need to find a point (x, y) so that x and y values of this point satisfy both equations in the system.*

- *What does it mean to satisfy both equations in the system?*

- *How would you find the solution?*

Discuss Jeff's solution with your students. Use this conversation to assess what kinds of assistance they will need as they work through the parts of the problem.

Tell students:

- *In this investigation, you will practice solving systems of linear equations symbolically. This is a helpful tool when you need to know the precise location of intersections of lines and not just estimates from a graph.*

Materials
- Transparencies 4.1A, 4.1B

Explore

Have students find the intersection points for their flight plans using symbolic methods.

Try to get struggling students to realize that the intersection point will have coordinates that satisfy both equations:

For groups who have obtained an intersection point, ask:

- *Do your results seem to match the graphic solution suggested by the diagram at the beginning of the investigation?*

Refer to the full Explore section of the Teacher Edition for challenge questions. When most students have attempted Question B, move on to the summary. Question B is a challenging part of this problem. It can be discussed as a whole class in the summary.

Have groups display their work and explain their thinking for Question A.

Then check the match between the groups' algebraically calculated results and the location of intersection points on the graph.

Discuss Question B as a whole group.

ACE Assignment Guide for Problem 4.1

Core 1–7

Other *Connections* 27–37, *Extensions* 61, and unassigned choices from previous problems

Adapted For suggestions about adapting Exercises 2–7 and other ACE exercises, see the CMP *Special Needs Handbook*.

Connecting to Prior Units 27–37: *Moving Straight Ahead*

Answers to Problem 4.1

A. 1. $0.3x - 2 = -2x + 14$, so $x \approx 6.96$. (6.96, 0.09)

2. (4.11, 5.78)

3. $x \approx 2.81$ and $y \approx 8.38$

4. $x \approx 5.21$ and $y \approx 7.42$

B. The strategy that will work consistently on these cases is to solve $ax + b = cx + d$ for x and then use that value and either individual original equation to calculate y. A formula for x will be $x = \frac{d - b}{a - c}$. You could reason to this formula as follows:

$ax + b = cx + d$

equivalent to $ax - cx = d - b$

equivalent to $(a - c)x = d - b$

equivalent to $x = \frac{d - b}{a - c}$

C. If a flight controller spotted two planes headed toward a collision, he/she could ask one or the other to change altitude, slow or increase its speed, or change course heading.

The $ax + by = c$ Case

Goal

- Develop and use the strategy for solving systems of linear equations by solving each individual equation for the same variable

Some systems of linear equations appear in what is often called standard form, but can be easily rewritten as a pair of equations in the "$y = \ldots$" form and solved by the method of Problem 4.1. Problem 4.2 highlights such cases, and Questions A and B of this problem ask students to use what they know about equivalence transformations of linear equations to develop skill in solving for y in terms of x or vice versa. Then Question C asks them to use that cue to solve several standard linear systems.

Launch 4.2

You might begin work on this problem by using the Getting Ready to ask students to comment on similarities and differences in the following two systems—one that is very much like those they solved in Problem 4.1.

$$\begin{cases} y = 3x - 30 \\ y = 14 - x \end{cases} \qquad \begin{cases} 3x - y = 30 \\ x + y = 14 \end{cases}$$

Suggested Questions

- *What does it mean to solve the system of equations like the system on the left?* (Solving a system means the same thing as finding the intersection point(s) for the lines represented by the equations involved in the system. It means finding the value(s) of (x, y) that satisfy both equations.)

- *Which system seems easier to solve?* (Answers will vary, but it seems likely that students will pick the first system because they've just worked on such systems.)

If students do not point out that the systems are equivalent, ask them directly whether this is so. Because each of the equations is replaced with an equivalent equation, the system is also equivalent. The intention of this problem is to have students solve systems of linear equations in

standard form (like the one on the right) by converting to slope-intercept form (on the left).

Have students write the standard form equations in $x = ky + c$ form:

$$\begin{cases} x = \dfrac{y}{3} + 10 \\ x = -y + 14 \end{cases}$$

Have students work in pairs or other small groups.

Explore 4.2

Check students' progress on Questions A–D to see how they are doing and how they are thinking about their solutions.

In particular, if students seem able to correctly transform the given "$ax + by = c$" forms into equivalent "$y = mx + b$" or "$x = ky + c$" forms, ask them how they know that their results are equivalent to the original equations.

For Question B, ask students if they could have solved both equations for the x instead if they solved for y first or vice versa. If students are solving all the equations for y first in C, encourage them to do one system by solving for x.

Suggested Question

- *Does it matter which variable you solve the equations for? Explain.* [It doesn't matter since you are trying to find a point (x, y) that satisfies both equations in the system. If you solve both equations for x first, the only difference is that you end up with an equation in the variable y to solve. When you find this value for y, substitute back in to either of the original equations to get the value for x.]

Solving for x and setting the expressions in y equal is the reverse of the work done in Problem 4.1, in which students solved an equation where the variable was x and they substituted this value into either equation to find the corresponding y-value.

Have students share their results for Questions A and B, including explaining the steps in their reasoning. Examples that require both addition and multiplication or division transformation steps will be vulnerable to errors. You might be prepared to offer some flawed work to ask students to spot the error. For example, ask: *Are the following derivations correct?*
(note that only the third one is)

$$6x + 2y = 8$$
$$2y = 8 - 6x$$
$$y = 4 - 6x$$

$$6x + 2y = 8$$
$$3x + y = 8$$
$$y = 8 - 3x$$

$$6x + 2y = 8$$
$$3x + y = 4$$
$$y = 4 - 3x$$

You might choose to work through one such example as part of the lesson launch to head off some likely errors. Another strategy would be to stop the class for a mid-lesson check when it appears that most groups have completed Question A and before they get into Question B.

Ask students to offer their ideas for how to look at linear systems and decide how to proceed. Give some linear systems as examples that they can use to explain.

Suggested Questions

- *Examine each system. Explain how you might proceed to solve each system.*

- *Is it easier to solve first for y or for x?*

$$\begin{cases} 3y = x - 9 \\ 2y = -1 - x \end{cases} \qquad \begin{cases} 2y = -3x - 9 \\ y = -4 - 2x \end{cases}$$

$$\begin{cases} 3y = 6x - 9 \\ -10y = -6 - 2x \end{cases} \qquad \begin{cases} -4y = x - 8 \\ x = -1 - y \end{cases}$$

- *To use this strategy of solving for the same variable and setting the two expressions equal, what criteria do you look for in the system?*

It is important to create a permanent record of students' ideas. Students should be able to refer back to these ideas when they practice their new algorithms. To this end, you could write up students' ideas on poster paper to be displayed in the room. Or write the ideas on the board and have students copy them in their notebooks.

4.2 The $ax + by = c$ Case

Mathematical Goal

- Develop and use the strategy for solving systems of linear equations by solving each individual equation for the same variable

Launch

Begin work on this problem by using the Getting Ready to ask students to comment on similarities and differences between systems expressed in standard form and those in slope-intercept form.

- *Which system seems easier to solve?*

If students do not point out that the systems are equivalent, ask them directly whether this is so. Because each of the equations is replaced with an equivalent equation, the system is also equivalent. The intention of this problem is to have students solve systems of linear equations in standard form by converting to slope-intercept form.

Have students work in pairs or other small groups.

Materials
- Poster paper (optional)
- Transparency 4.2

Explore

Check students' progress on Questions A–D to see how they are doing and how they are thinking about their solutions.

In particular, if students seem able to correctly transform the given "$ax + by = c$" forms into equivalent "$y = mx + b$" or "$x = ky + c$" forms, ask them how they know that their results are equivalent to the original equations.

For Question B, ask students if they could have solved both equations for the x instead if they solved for y first or vice versa. If students are solving all the equations for y first in Question C, encourage them to do one system by solving for x.

Summarize

Have students share their results for Questions A and B, including explaining the steps in their reasoning. Examples that require both addition and multiplication or division transformation steps will be vulnerable to errors. You might be prepared to offer some flawed work to ask students to spot the error.

You might choose to work through one such example as part of the lesson launch to head off some likely errors. Another strategy would be to stop the class for a mid-lesson check when it appears that most groups have completed Question A and before they get into Question B.

Ask students to offer their ideas for how to look at linear systems.

Materials
- Student notebooks
- Poster paper (optional)

continued on next page

Summarize continued

It is important to create a permanent record of students' ideas. Students should be able to refer back to these ideas when they practice their new algorithms. To this end, you could write up students' ideas on poster paper to be displayed in the room. Or write the ideas on the board and have students copy them in their notebooks.

ACE Assignment Guide for Problem 4.2

Differentiated Instruction
Solutions for All Learners

Core 8–14
Other *Connections* 38–46, *Extensions* 62, and unassigned choices from previous problems

Adapted For suggestions about adapting ACE exercises, see the CMP *Special Needs Handbook*.
Connecting to Prior Units 38–43: *Moving Straight Ahead*

Answers to Problem 4.2

A. Students will choose their forms differently. Both forms are offered as answers here.

1. $y = -x + 3$
$x = -y + 3$

2. $y = x + 5$
$x = y - 5$

3. $y = -2x - 1$
$x = -\frac{1}{2}y - \frac{1}{2}$

4. $y = \frac{1}{2}x - 4$
$x = 2y + 8$

5. $y = -\frac{3}{2}x + 2$
$x = \frac{-2}{3}y + \frac{4}{3}$

6. $y = \frac{1}{4}x + \frac{5}{2}$
$x = 4y - 10$

7. Usually students prefer to avoid the fractions created when dividing is necessary to make the coefficient of x (or y) equal to 1. They may say they prefer to isolate the variable whose coefficient is 1 or -1, if that is possible.

B. 1. $x = -1, y = 4$

  2. $x = 11, y = 3$

  3. $x = 3, y = 2$

  4. Infinitely many solutions; equations are equivalent.

C. 1. Solving both equations for the same variable in terms of the other variable is particularly efficient when the coefficients of one variable are both 1 or -1, or if one of the equations is already in the desired form.

  2. Solve each equation for either x or y. Then use the equality of the two expressions created ($x =$ expression in terms of y, for example) to make an equation in one variable. Solve this equation and substitute your solution back into either of the original equations to find the other variable.

D. 1. Two equations are equivalent if they have the same solutions.

  2. Solving a system of linear equations means finding a solution that is common to both equations in the system.

Solving Systems of Linear Equations by Substitution

Goal

- Develop and use the strategy for solving systems of linear equations by substitution

One general technique for solving systems of equations (not only linear systems) is to substitute one expression for another. For solving linear systems with two equations and two unknowns, this substitution strategy is particularly helpful when one of the equations already expresses one variable in terms of the other or if it is easy to transform one equation into that form.

Alternate Launch

You could launch the problem by challenging students to find a third way to solve a system.

$$\begin{cases} y = 2x + 5 \\ 4x + 3y = 25 \end{cases}$$

Suggested Questions

- *Here's a system that is a mixture of the two previous types. Can you think of yet a third way one could solve systems, when they look like this?*

You might try such a challenge to launch the work on Problem 4.3, but the problem is also set up to lead students more directly to useful strategies through analysis of worked examples.

In the "analyzing-worked-examples" teaching strategy, we ask the students to imagine that they have come across someone else's work on a problem and to figure out whether the work is correct and how the other person might have been thinking about the problem and its solution.

Launch 4.3

If you did not use the more open alternate launch, you can use the Getting Ready task to launch the problem. By this point in the algebra strand, the end of this worked example should not be problematic for students. The difficult part is likely to be the transition from step 1 to step 2. In this transition, we need to change the way we think about the linear equations in the system. In general, we think of an equation of the form $y = mx + b$ as a dynamic relationship involving many possible (x, y) pairs. When we have two distinct, nonparallel linear relationships in a system, there is one single point that solves the system. When we solve a system, we are looking for this one point; one (x, y) pair.

Help students understand that they are looking for a single (x, y) pair. Then we can think of the two equations in the system as putting constraints on the x and y values. We are looking for an x and y such that both equations are true.

When we substitute in step 2, we are substituting equals for equals. There is some point (x, y) such that $y = 3x - 5$, so we can substitute $3x - 5$ for y. We are left with an equation only in x, which students know how to solve.

Have students work in pairs.

Explore 4.3

You might assign different systems in Question A to different student pairs and ask them to prepare a presentation of their results that shows the steps in their reasoning.

For students working on the systems in Question A, parts (4) and (5), if they are having difficulty you may want to ask them why they think that this problem is different than the one they explored in Problem 4.2. Have them try to graph the two equations in the system. Also suggest they try another system from the remaining parts of Question A.

Have students present their solutions and reasoning to the systems in task A.

Suggested Question

- *What does it mean to say that your point (x, y) is a solution to the system?*

- *How do you know that your solution is correct? How can you check?*

- *How is the substitution method different from and similar to the method you used to solve systems algebraically in Problems 4.1 and 4.2?*

Discuss Question B and have the students who worked on Question A, parts (4) and (5), contribute to this discussion.

Have students give tips to solving a system using the substitution method. Write these tips on a piece of poster paper or on the board and have students put the tips in their notebooks.

Discuss Question C as a class.

- *Would you use the substitution method or some other method to solve the following systems?*

$$\begin{cases} 4x + y = 6 \\ -3x + y = 1 \end{cases} \text{ and } \begin{cases} 2x + y = 3 \\ -3x - 7y = 1 \end{cases}$$

Answers will vary to this question, but a likely answer is that the first system is easy to solve by the method of Problem 4.2. This is because the coefficient of y is 1 in both equations, so solving for y is straightforward. However, both methods are relatively easy to apply to this system. The second system, however, results in inconvenient fractions whether we solve for x or for y. In this case, substitution keeps the numbers nicer and may lead to fewer errors.

The choice of which method to use is a matter of preference though some methods require fewer steps. Observe students' reasoning for why they would choose to use a particular method.

4.3 Solving Systems of Linear Equations by Substitution

Mathematical Goal

- Develop and use the strategy for solving systems of linear equations by substitution.

Launch

Launch work on this problem with the Getting Ready task.

Help students to understand that they are looking for a single (x, y) pair. Then we can think of the two equations in the system as putting constraints on the x and y values. We are looking for an x and y such that both equations are true.

When we substitute in step 2, we are substituting equals for equals. Have students work in pairs.

Materials
- Transparencies 4.3A, 4.3B

Explore

You might assign different systems in Question A to different student pairs and ask them to prepare a presentation of their results that shows the steps in their reasoning.

For students working on the systems in Question A, parts (4) and (5), if they are having difficulty you may want to ask them why they think that this problem is different than the one they explored in Problem 4.2. Have them try to graph the two equations in the system. Also suggest they try another system from the remaining parts of Question A.

Summarize

Have students present their solutions and reasoning to the systems in Question A.

- *What does it mean to say that your point (x, y) is a solution to the system? How do you know that your solution is correct? How can you check? How is the substitution method different from the method you used to solve systems algebraically in Problems 4.1 and 4.2?*

Discuss Question B and have the students who worked on Question A, parts (4) and (5) contribute to this discussion.

Have students give tips to solving a system using the substitution method. Write these tips on a piece of poster paper or on the board and have students put the tips in their notebooks.

Discuss Question C as a class.

The choice of which method to use is a matter of preference though some methods require fewer steps. Observe students' reasoning for why they would choose to use a particular method.

Materials
- Student notebooks
- Poster paper (optional)

ACE Assignment Guide for Problem 4.3

Core 15–20
Other *Connections* 47–50, *Extensions* 63, and unassigned choices from previous problems

Adapted For suggestions about adapting ACE exercises, see the CMP *Special Needs Handbook*.
Connecting to Prior Units 47: *Filling and Wrapping*; 48, 49: *Say It With Symbols*; 50: *Stretching and Shrinking*; 50: *Kaleidoscopes, Hubcaps, and Mirrors*

Answers to Problem 4.3

A. 1. Possible sequences:

Solve the first equation for y in terms of x.

$$x - 2(-2x - 1) = 12$$
$$5x + 2 = 12$$
$$x = 2$$

$$y = -2(2) - 1$$
$$y = -5$$

Solve the second equation for x in terms of y.

$$2(2y + 12) + y = -1$$
$$5y + 24 = -1$$
$$y = -5$$

$$x = 2(-5) + 12$$
$$x = 2$$

2. In this system it is probably easier to solve the first equation for y in terms of x, getting $y = -2x + 3$. The solution to the system is $x = 2$ and $y = -1$.

3. This system can be solved by substitution by solving for x in terms of y or for y in terms of x in the first equation or by solving for x in terms of y in the second equation.

The solution is $x = -\frac{10}{3}$ and $y = \frac{5}{3}$.

4. In this system it is probably easiest to solve the first equation for y in terms of x. When this relationship is substituted in the second equation, the resulting equation $6x + 2(-3x + 4) = 7$ yields $0x + 8 = 7$. No values of x satisfy this equation, so the system has an empty solution set. This puzzling result can be explained by graphing the two given equations and discovering that the graphs are parallel lines.

5. In this system one could solve either original equation for y in terms of x and then substitute in the other. Trying the first equation, one gets $y = -1.5x + 5$. The substitution in the second equation yields $-6x - 4(-1.5x + 5) = -20$. Proceeding to solve this equation in x one arrives at $0x - 20 = -20$ or simply $-20 = -20$. Since this equation is true regardless of the value of x, the equation has an infinite number of solution pairs.

This solution situation can be explained by graphing the two lines and discovering that the graphs are identical. Thus any ordered pair (x, y) that satisfies one equation will certainly satisfy the other.

This situation does not mean that any pair (x, y) will satisfy the system, only that any pair satisfying one of the equations will also satisfy the other.

6. Solve either individual equation for x in terms of y or vice versa. The solution is $x = 7.5$ and $y = 5.5$.

B. 1. System (4) corresponds to two parallel lines and system (5) corresponds to identical lines.

2. In $y = mx + b$ form, the systems are

$$\begin{cases} y = -3x + 4 \\ y = -3x + 3.5 \end{cases} \text{ and } \begin{cases} y = -1.5x + 5 \\ y = -1.5x + 5 \end{cases}$$

The first two lines are parallel and disjoint; the second two are identical.

C. 1. See discussion of solution methods in the Summarize section.

a. $\left(\frac{5}{7}, 3\frac{1}{7}\right)$

b. $\left(\frac{20}{17}, \frac{11}{17}\right)$

2. In system (a), it is easy to write each equation in $y = ax + b$ form. This makes the equivalent form method useful.

In system (b), the arithmetic becomes more tedious to use the equivalent form method. However, the first equation is easy to write in $y = ax + b$ form and then to use substitution.

Goals

- Use linear combinations to solve systems of linear equations

- Choose strategically among the three algebraic methods which to use for a particular system of linear equations

Although many of the systems involving two equations and two unknowns can be solved readily by graphic or substitution methods or by simply solving each equation for y in terms of x and setting the resulting expressions equal, the most efficient and informative strategy for solving linear systems in the long run (i.e., for systems with more equations and more unknowns) is the method often called linear combinations. This strategy relies on two basic principles about linear equations.

- First, if both sides of a linear equation are multiplied by the same number, the solution set of the resulting equation will be identical to that of the original.

- Second, if one equation in a system is replaced by the result of adding one of the other equations to it, the resulting system will have the same solution(s) as the original.

Mathematics Background

For background on solving systems by linear combination, see pages 7–9.

Launch 4.4 Questions A–C

Explain to students that in this problem they will learn another way to solve systems of linear equations algebraically.

Two of the most useful principles for transforming equations into equivalent algebraic forms involve "adding (or subtracting) equals to equals" and "multiplying (or dividing) equals by equals."

Write the following equation on the board or overhead.

For example, you know in arithmetic that $5 + 3 = 8$, so:

$$(5 + 3) + 3.14 = 8 + 3.14 \text{ and}$$
$$12.5(5 + 3) = 12.5(8)$$

You may want to write the $5 + 3$ and the 8 in the first equation in the same color marker and then the 3.14 on both sides for the first equation in a different color, to illustrate that equals (3.14) was added to equals $(5 + 3$ and $8)$. Similarly, for the second equation, write the $5 + 3$ and 8 in one color and the 12.5's in a different color.

These facts about numbers and operations can be used to develop another way for solving linear systems algebraically. In this new strategy, you will combine the separate linear equations into one equation with only one unknown.

Start the students on exploration of the worked example in the Getting Ready box. This doesn't require multiplying either of the given equations by a constant. Challenge students to see whether the work yields the correct solution for the system and, if so, why the indicated manipulations work.

Have a discussion of their ideas stimulated by questions like these:

Suggested Questions

- Is the proposed solution correct? (Yes, the results check.)

It's a little harder to see algebraically why there is only one solution. The uniqueness of the solution is evident from the graphs: the lines cross at a single point.

- *Why do you suppose the solution is the same for the given system involving two equations and the single equation* $(x - y) + (x + y) = 4 + 5$? (Whatever values of x and y satisfy both equations then this single equation results from adding equals to equals. That is, if $A = B$ and $C = D$, then $A + C = B + D$.)

- *What very fortunate result followed from adding the two equations?* (We are left with an equation in one variable: x. Therefore, we know the x-value of the solution to the original system.)

To further set the mathematical context, you might have a discussion with students like the one in the TE introduction to this problem, connecting the symbolic work to graphical solutions.

Have the students work in pairs. Depending on time and your students' proficiency, you may want to split the work on this problem into two days. On day 1, you could work through Questions A–C, and on day 2, Questions D–F. Even if you have the time to work the whole problem in a day, it makes sense to have a whole-group discussion after students have completed Question C.

Explore 4.4 Questions A–C

Have students work on the systems of Question A with the goal of seeing how addition (or subtraction) of equations can lead to a single equation in one variable.

If students are having trouble getting started have them explain to you the steps in the worked example at the beginning of the problem.

Suggested Questions

- *So, in the worked example, we added equals to equals. How can you use the same steps to solve the system in Question A, part (1)?* (Since $-x + 4y = 3$, you could add something equal to both sides. In this case $x + 2y = 5$, so we could add $x + 2y$ to the left side and 5 to the right side.)

For Question A, parts (2) and (3), students need to subtract equals from equals. Ask students:

- *We know that $3 + 5 = 8$, so we can subtract any expression from the right side of the equation as long as we subtract an equal expression from the right side.*

- *What types of quantities can we subtract from both sides of this equation?* (Answers will vary.)

- *Since we know that $2 + 4$ equals 6 can we subtract $2 + 4$ from $3 + 5$ and 6 from 8? Is this equation still true?* (Yes; $3 + 5 - (2 + 4) = 8 - 6$. Ask students if they could have written the equation as $3 + 5 - 2 + 4 = 8 - 6$. This will help get them thinking about using parentheses when they are talking about subtracting equal quantities from equal quantities and order of operations.)

- *How can we use this idea—of equals minus equals giving us equals—to solve the systems in Question A, parts (2) and (3)?*

Summarize 4.4 Questions A–C

Have students present their solutions and explanations to Question A.

Suggested Questions

- *For Question A, part (2), can you solve the system by adding $5x + 3y$ to $2x + 3y$ and -8 to 4? Explain.* (No; In order to get an equation in one variable, we need to subtract so that the y terms disappear from the equations.)

- *How do you make the decision whether to add or to subtract?* (Figure out whether you can make the coefficient of a variable zero by subtracting or adding.)

Once you feel students have the basic idea of adding and subtracting to form convenient combinations, discuss Question B to set up the rest of the problem.

The examples in Question B illustrate a strategy for solving systems of linear equations called the linear combinations method. The idea, like in other strategies you've used in earlier problems (solving both equations for y and setting results equal or solving one equation for y and substituting in the other), is to combine the given conditions into a single equation with only one unknown.

Sometimes the given equations will yield to the addition (or subtraction) approach immediately like the systems in Question A and Question B. But in other cases you might need to do some preparation.

- *Why does the graph of system B and the equation formed by adding help to solve this system?*

Launch 4.4 Questions D–F

Have students examine the systems in Question D.

- *Is it possible to use the addition or subtraction approach on these equations in Question D?*

- *Find several pairs of integers x and y satisfying $2x + y = 5$.* [Some possibilities are $(0, 5), (1, 3), (2, 1), (3, -1)$, etc.]

- *Now find several pairs of integers x and y satisfying $6x + 3y = 15$.*

- *Why do you suppose solutions to the first equation turned out to be the same as solutions to the second?*

- *In the equations in Question D, you may need to change one or both of the equations into equivalent equations before you can work with them.*

Explore 4.4 Questions D–F

For students who are having difficulty with the equations in Question D, ask:

Suggested Questions

- *Can you apply the method of subtraction or addition like you did in Question A? Why or why not?*

- *How can you make the coefficient of one of the variables zero so that you have an equation in one variable to solve? What coefficients for the variable would you need?*

- *Is there a number that you could multiply one of the equations by so that you could get that coefficient?*

- *What would the new system look like?*

As students work, ask them questions about their strategies:

- *How did you find that solution?*

- *How do you know your solution is correct?*

- *How do you know your solution is the only solution?*

Make sure students are preparing presentations of their work and their reasoning for the summary.

Summarize 4.4 Questions D–F

Suggested Questions

- *In Question B, there are two systems given. How do you know that the systems are equivalent?* (The systems are equivalent because the second equation $4x - y = 6$ is replaced by an equivalent equation $8x - 2y = 12$. The equations $4x - y = 6$ and $8x - 2y = 12$ are equivalent because two times the equation $4x - y = 6$ equals the equation $8x - 2y = 12$.)

- *Can we multiply any equation* ax + by = c *by a number and get an equivalent equation with the same graph and same solutions? How do you know?* (Yes; by the properties of equality, you can multiply both sides of the equation by the same value and maintain equality.)

- *Can we divide any equation* ax + by = c *by a number and get an equivalent equation? How do you know?* (Yes; by the properties of equality, you can divide both sides of the equation by the same value and maintain equality.)

After a group of students present their work on Question D, ask the class:

- *Did anyone solve that system differently using linear combinations? How would you check that the solution is correct?*

Discuss other ways to solve the systems. For example, you may want to discuss how to solve one of the systems graphically using a graphing calculator, another by putting the equations in $y = ax + b$ or $x = cy + d$ form and another using combinations.

Have students discuss their solution methods for the systems in Question E. Make sure that students are explicit about which method they use, as well as how they decide which method to use. This will help expose other students to important ideas.

For Question E, have students explain what method they chose and why. You are looking for reasoning that suggests the student(s) are beginning to be strategic about choices. For example, some students may choose equivalent form for part (a) because the coefficients of y are $+1$ and -1, both of which allow easy computation to get

$$\begin{cases} y = 5 - 2x \\ y = 3x - 15 \end{cases}$$

However, the combination method immediately gives you $5x = 20$ and $x = 4$, so $y = -3$. This is even faster and easier.

Help students see that any method can be used on any of the systems, but the arithmetic may be messy. A strategic choice can make the work much easier.

4.4 Solving Systems of Linear Equations by Combination

Mathematical Goals

- Use linear combinations to solve systems of linear equations

- Choose strategically among the three algebraic methods which to use for a particular system of linear equations

Launch

Demonstrate the two properties of equations pertinent to this problem using numbers. Start the students on the example in the Getting Ready.

- *Is the proposed solution correct?*
- *Why do you suppose the solution proceeds from the given system involving two equations to the single equation (x − y) + (x + y) = 4 + 5?*

Have the students work in pairs. Depending on time and your students' proficiency, you may want to split the work on this problem into two days.

Materials
- Transparency 4.4

Explore

Explore I (Questions A–C)

Have students work on Question A with the goal of seeing how addition (or subtraction) of equations can lead to a single equation in one variable.

Explore II (Questions D–F)

For students who are having difficulty with Question D, ask:

- *Can you apply the method of subtraction or addition like you did in Question A? Why or why not?*
- *How can you make the coefficient of one of the variables zero so that you have an equation in one variable to solve?*
- *What coefficients for the variable would you need?*

As students work, ask them questions about their strategies.

Summarize

Summarize (Questions A–C)

Have students present their solutions and explanations to Question A.

Once you feel students have the basic idea of forming convenient combinations, discuss Question B to set up the rest of the problem.

Summarize (Questions D–F)

Have students present their solutions. Discuss other ways to solve the systems, for example graphically or with different combinations.

Have students discuss their methods for solving Questions D and E.

Materials
- Student notebooks
- Poster paper (optional)

Vocabulary
- linear combinations

ACE Assignment Guide for Problem 4.4

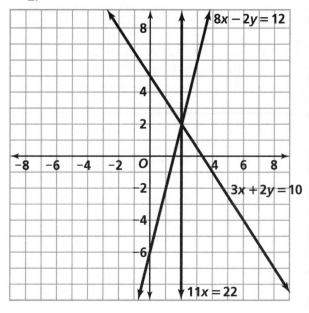

The graph of the new equation intersects the other graphs at their previous point of intersection.

2.

They all intersect at a unique common point.

3. The new equation is $x = 2$, which is the x-coordinate of the solution for the system.

Core 21–26

Other *Connections* 51–60, *Extensions* 64–67, and unassigned choices from previous problems

Adapted For suggestions about adapting ACE exercises, see the CMP *Special Needs Handbook*. **Connecting to Prior Units** 51–56: *Frogs, Fleas, and Painted Cubes; Growing, Growing, Growing; Thinking With Mathematical Models;* 57–60: *Say It With Symbols*

Answers to Problem 4.4

A. 1. $6y = 8$ or $y = \frac{4}{3}, x = 5 - 2(\frac{4}{3})$ or $x = \frac{7}{3}$

2. $3x = -12$ or $x = -4, 2(-4) + 3y = 4$ or $y = 4$

3. $3x = 3$ or $x = 1, 2(1) - 3y = 4$ or $y = -\frac{2}{3}$

B. 1. We have simply multiplied both sides of the second equation by 2. Every pair (x, y) satisfying the first equation will satisfy the second and vice versa.

2. $\begin{cases} 3x + 2y = 10 \\ 8x - 2y = 12 \end{cases}$

Therefore, $11x = 22$
$$x = 2$$
$$y = 2$$
$$(2, 2)$$

C. 1. $7x + y = 16$

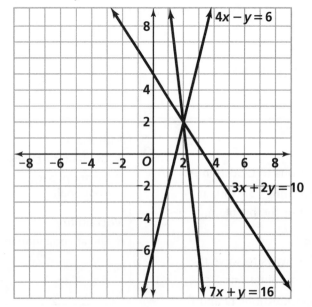

D. 1. The simplest strategy is probably to multiply the first equation by 3 (though other methods are correct, if less efficient). Then adding the two equations of the new system yields $9x = 27, x = 3$, and $y = -0.5$.

2. Here again, multiplying the first equation by 3 is probably the simplest and most efficient transformation to apply. Then subtracting the second equation from the first yields $5y = 10, y = 2$, and $x = -2$.

E. 1. Choices of solution method will vary. The solution to each system is listed.

    a. $(4, -3)$ **b.** $(6\frac{1}{2}, -\frac{3}{4})$

    c. $(2, \frac{1}{2})$

    d. The solution set is infinite. The two equations in the system are equivalent.

    e. The solution set is infinite. The two equations in the system are equivalent.

2. Strategies will vary.

F. One might notice that the second equation in each case is an integer multiple of the first.

**The student edition pages for this
investigation begin on the next page.**

Notes

Solving Systems of Linear Equations Symbolically

Every day of the year, thousands of airline flights crisscross the United States to connect large and small cities. Each flight follows a plan filed with air traffic control before take-off.

The flight paths of airplanes are not straight lines from take-off to landing. But parts of those paths are generally straight-line segments. At any hour of the day, the pattern of flight plans might look like the diagram below.

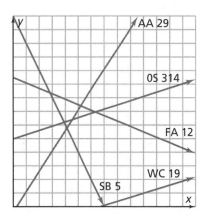

The diagram seems to show many potential mid-air collisions.

Why do you think such disasters almost never occur?

What information about flight paths is not shown on the diagram?

If planned flight paths are represented by equations, an air-traffic control system can calculate intersection points and warn of possible collisions. The equations for the flights in the diagram are shown in the table.

In this problem, you will explore a simplified air-traffic control system. You will ignore the height above the ground and time and consider only whether the flight paths of two planes intersect. These intersection points tell you which parts of the flight paths controllers need to examine more carefully to prevent collisions.

52   The Shapes of Algebra

Notes _____

_____

_____

_____

4.1 The $y = mx + b$ Case

The equations for the flight paths can be used to calculate the nine intersection points shown on the graph.

Getting Ready for Problem

A table of equations for the flight paths is at the right. To find the intersection of WC 19 and AA 29, you need to find the (x, y) pair that satisfies the system of linear equations below. (The bracket is a special notation used to indicate a system of equations.)

$$\begin{cases} y = 0.3x - 2 \\ y = 1.5x - 0.4 \end{cases}$$

Jeff writes the following to solve this system.

$$0.3x - 2 = 1.5x - 0.4$$
$$-1.2x = 1.6$$
$$x = \frac{1.6}{-1.2}$$
$$x = -\frac{4}{3}$$

Flight Paths

Airline/Flight	Equation
Apex Airlines Flight *AA 29*	$y = 1.5x - 0.4$
We-Care Air Flight *WC 19*	$y = 0.3x - 2$
Open Sky Airlines Flight *OS 314*	$y = 0.3x + 5$
Fly Away Airlines Flight *FA 12*	$y = -0.4x + 9.5$
Sky Bus Airlines Flight *SB 5*	$y = -2x + 14$

- Explain Jeff's reasoning.
- What does $x = -\frac{4}{3}$ tell you?
- How can you find the y-coordinate of the intersection point?

Problem 4.1 The $y = mx + b$ Case

A. Write and solve systems to find the intersections of these flight plans.

   1. WC 19 and SB 5   **2.** SB 5 and AA 29

   3. SB 5 and FA 12   **4.** FA 12 and AA 29

B. Study the work you did in Question A. Describe a strategy for solving any system of this form shown below.

$$\begin{cases} y = ax + b \\ y = cx + d \end{cases}$$

C. What could an air-traffic controller do if two flight plans intersect?

ACE **Homework starts on page 59.**

STUDENT PAGE

Notes _____

_____

_____

_____

The $ax + by = c$ **Case**

When a system of linear equations is in $y = mx + b$ form, it is easy to write a single linear equation with the same solution as the system.

$$\begin{cases} y = ax + b \\ y = cx + d \end{cases} \text{ becomes } ax + b = cx + d.$$

The equations in a linear system are not always given in $y = mx + b$ form. In this problem, you'll consider systems of this form:

$$\begin{cases} ax + by = c \\ dx + ey = f \end{cases}$$

Getting Ready for Problem

Suppose the solution to a situation requires you to find values of x and y that satisfy the system:

$$\begin{cases} 3x - y = 30 \\ x + y = 14 \end{cases}$$

One useful strategy for solving a linear system is to rewrite the equations in familiar equivalent forms.

- Write each equation in $y = mx + b$ form. Then, find a solution using the method you learned in Problem 4.1.

- Write each equation in $x = ky + c$ form. Then, find a solution. Are the solutions the same?

- Why might you expect both methods to give the same solution?

Problem 4.2 Solving Systems by Writing Equivalent Forms

A. Decide whether it is easier to write each equation in equivalent $y = mx + b$ form or equivalent $x = ky + c$ form. Then, write each equation in the form you chose.

1. $x + y = 3$ **2.** $x - y = -5$

3. $2x + y = -1$ **4.** $x - 2y = 8$

5. $9x + 6y = 12$ **6.** $-x + 4y = 10$

7. In parts (1)–(6), how did you decide which form to use?

Notes _____

_____

_____

_____

B. Solve each system by writing the equations in $y = mx + b$ or $x = ky + c$ form and then using the strategy from Problem 4.1.

1. $\begin{cases} x + y = 3 \\ x - y = -5 \end{cases}$

2. $\begin{cases} 3x - y = 30 \\ x + y = 14 \end{cases}$

3. $\begin{cases} x + 6y = 15 \\ -x + 4y = 5 \end{cases}$

4. $\begin{cases} x - y = -5 \\ -2x + 2y = 10 \end{cases}$

C. Look back over your work from Question B.

   1. What do you notice about the systems that makes this method a good one to use?

   2. Describe the steps needed in using this method to solve a system.

D. 1. What does it mean for two equations to be equivalent?

   2. What does it mean to solve a linear system?

 ACE Homework starts on page 59.

4.3 Solving Systems by Substitution

Writing the equations in a linear system in $y = mx + b$ or $x = ky + c$ form is not always easy. Sometimes the arithmetic becomes messy.

For example, consider how you would solve this system.

$$\begin{cases} 3x - y = 5 \\ 2x + 5y = -8 \end{cases}$$

Solve both equations for y to get $y = mx + b$ form.

$$3x - y = 5 \qquad\qquad 2x + 5y = -8$$
$$-y = 5 - 3x \qquad\qquad 5y = -8 - 2x$$
$$y = 3x - 5 \qquad\qquad y = -\frac{8}{5} - \frac{2}{5}x$$

Set the right sides of the equations equal.

$$3x - 5 = -\frac{8}{5} - \frac{2}{5}x$$
$$15x - 25 = -8 - 2x$$
$$17x = 17$$
$$x = 1$$

In this problem, you'll look at another solution method that is easier in many cases.

Notes _____

_____

_____

_____

Check the reasoning in this method of solving a system of linear equations by *substitution* and see if you can explain why it works.

1. The system $\begin{cases} 3x - y = 5 \\ 2x + 5y = -8 \end{cases}$ is equivalent to the system $\begin{cases} y = 3x - 5 \\ 2x + 5y = -8. \end{cases}$

2. From that fact, any solution should satisfy $2x + 5(3x - 5) = -8$. Why is this equation an advantage over the two-equation system?

3. Solving this single equation for x, you get:

$$2x + 15x - 25 = -8$$
$$17x = 17$$
$$x = 1$$

4. Then $y = 3(1) - 5 = -2$.

5. The ordered pair $(1, -2)$ satisfies both equations in the original system:

$$3(1) - (-2) = 5 \qquad\qquad 2(1) + 5(-2) = -8$$

So $(1, -2)$ is the solution.

- Does this strategy produce the *only* solution for both equations in the original system? Why?

- Which solution strategy do you think is easier for this system, writing the equations in $y = ax + b$ form and setting them equal or using substitution? Why?

Problem 4.3 Solving Systems by Substitution

A. Use substitution to solve each system.

1. $\begin{cases} 2x + y = -1 \\ x - 2y = 12 \end{cases}$ **2.** $\begin{cases} 4x + 2y = 6 \\ -3x - 7y = 1 \end{cases}$ **3.** $\begin{cases} x - y = -5 \\ -x + 4y = 10 \end{cases}$

4. $\begin{cases} 3x + y = 4 \\ 6x + 2y = 7 \end{cases}$ **5.** $\begin{cases} 3x + 2y = 10 \\ -6x - 4y = -20 \end{cases}$ **6.** $\begin{cases} x + y = 13 \\ x - y = 2 \end{cases}$

B. You may have been puzzled by the solution to two of the systems in Question A. Complete parts (1) and (2) for each of these two systems.

1. Graph the two lines to see if you can make sense of the situation.

2. Write both equations in $y = mx + b$ form to see if this helps you understand the results.

Notes _____

_____

_____

_____

C. 1. Decide whether writing in equivalent form or substituting would be easier for solving the system. Then, solve the system.

a. $\begin{cases} 4x + y = 6 \\ -3x + y = 1 \end{cases}$ b. $\begin{cases} 2x + y = 3 \\ -3x + 7y = 1 \end{cases}$

2. For each system, explain why you chose the solution method.

 ACE Homework starts on page 59.

4.4 Solving Systems by Combination

You have already developed some useful strategies for solving a simple linear equation like $3x + 5 = 10$. You know that you can add or subtract the same quantity on both sides and preserve equality.

The same is true for multiplication or division. These ideas, called the *Properties of Equality,* can help you develop another method for solving linear equations. This method involves combining separate linear equations into one equation with only one variable.

Getting Ready for Problem 4.4

These steps show the *combination method* for solving $\begin{cases} x - y = 4 \\ x + y = 5. \end{cases}$

If $x - y = 4$ and $x + y = 5$, then	
$(x - y) + (x + y) = 4 + 5$	(1)
$2x = 9$	(2)
$x = 4.5$	(3)
$x + y = 5$	(4)
$4.5 + y = 5$	(5)
$y = 0.5$	(6)

- Give reasons for steps 1–5.
- Why is adding the two original equations an advantage?
- Would subtracting the two original equations work just as well?

Notes _____

_____

_____

_____

A. Use the combination method to solve these linear systems.

1. $\begin{cases} -x + 4y = 3 \\ x + 2y = 5 \end{cases}$ **2.** $\begin{cases} 2x + 3y = 4 \\ 5x + 3y = -8 \end{cases}$ **3.** $\begin{cases} 2x - 3y = 4 \\ 5x - 3y = 7 \end{cases}$

B. 1. Explain why System B is equivalent to System A.

System A	System B
$\begin{cases} 3x + 2y = 10 \\ 4x - y = 6 \end{cases}$	$\begin{cases} 3x + 2y = 10 \\ 8x - 2y = 12 \end{cases}$

2. Rewriting System A as System B is a possible first step in solving the system by the combination method. Complete this solution process by combining the two equations in System B.

C. 1. Add the two equations in System A. Graph both equations in System A and the new equation you made by adding. What do the three equations have in common?

2. Graph System B and the new equation you made by adding. What do the three equations have in common?

3. Why does the graph you made with System B and the new equation help to solve the system?

D. In parts (1) and (2), write an equivalent system that is easy to solve by combining equations. Then find the solution. Check your work by solving the system with a different method.

1. $\begin{cases} 2x + 2y = 5 \\ 3x - 6y = 12 \end{cases}$ **2.** $\begin{cases} x + 3y = 4 \\ 3x + 4y = 2 \end{cases}$

E. 1. Decide whether equivalent form, substitution, or combination would be easiest for solving the system. Then, solve the system.

a. $\begin{cases} 2x + y = 5 \\ 3x - y = 15 \end{cases}$ **b.** $\begin{cases} x + 2y = 5 \\ x - 6y = 11 \end{cases}$ **c.** $\begin{cases} 2x + 6y = 7 \\ 3x - 2y = 5 \end{cases}$

d. $\begin{cases} 2x + y = 5 \\ -4x - 2y = -10 \end{cases}$ **e.** $\begin{cases} x + 2y = 5 \\ 3x + 6y = 15 \end{cases}$

2. For each system in part (1), explain how you decided which solution method to use.

F. Two of the systems in Question E did not have single solutions. How could you have predicted this before you started to solve them?

ACE **Homework starts on page 59.**

Notes _____

_____

_____

_____

Applications

1. The diagram shows ferry routes between points surrounding a harbor.
The distance between grid lines is 500 feet.

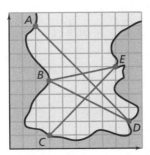

a. Call the bottom left corner on the grid the origin. Match each
route with the equation that describes it.

Route	Equation
A to D	$y = 0.2x + 2{,}200$
B to D	$y = x - 1{,}000$
B to E	$y = -x + 5{,}500$
C to E	$y = -0.5x + 3{,}250$

Homework
Help **O**nline
PHSchool.com
For: Help with Exercise 1
Web Code: ape-7401

b. Find the coordinates of the intersection points of the four routes.

Notes _____

_____

_____

_____

Solve each system.

Go Online
PHSchool.com

For: Multiple-Choice Skills
Practice
Web Code: apa-7454

2. $\begin{cases} y = 6x + 4 \\ y = 4x - 2 \end{cases}$ 3. $\begin{cases} y = 3x + 7 \\ y = 5x - 7 \end{cases}$ 4. $\begin{cases} y = -2x - 9 \\ y = 12x + 19 \end{cases}$

5. $\begin{cases} y = -x + 16 \\ y = -7x - 8 \end{cases}$ 6. $\begin{cases} y = 17x - 6 \\ y = 12x + 44 \end{cases}$ 7. $\begin{cases} y = -20x + 14 \\ y = -8x - 44 \end{cases}$

For Exercises 8–13, write the equation in $y = mx + b$ form.

8. $4x + 6y + 12 = 0$ 9. $-7x + 9y + 4 = 0$

10. $-4x - 2y - 6 = 0$ 11. $-x + 4y = 0$

12. $2x - 2y + 2 = 0$ 13. $25x + 5y - 15 = 0$

14. Write the equations in Exercises 8–13 in $x = ny + c$ form.

Solve the system by using substitution.

15. $\begin{cases} 3x + 4y = 9 \\ y = x - 3 \end{cases}$ 16. $\begin{cases} 8x - 14y = 5 \\ x = 3y \end{cases}$ 17. $\begin{cases} 12x + 4 = 8y \\ y = x - 7 \end{cases}$

18. $\begin{cases} y = 2x - 1 \\ 4x + 6y = 10 \end{cases}$ 19. $\begin{cases} x = 7y - 10 \\ 3x - 2y = 8 \end{cases}$ 20. $\begin{cases} 7x - 2y = 5 \\ x = y \end{cases}$

Solve the system by using the combination method.

21. $\begin{cases} 3x - 2y = 12 \\ -3x + 8y = -6 \end{cases}$ 22. $\begin{cases} 4x + 9y = 7 \\ 4x - 9y = 9 \end{cases}$ 23. $\begin{cases} 12x - 14y = -8 \\ -8x - 14y = 52 \end{cases}$

24. $\begin{cases} 5x + 15y = 10 \\ 5x - 10y = -40 \end{cases}$ 25. $\begin{cases} -6x - 4y = 21 \\ -6x + 3y = 0 \end{cases}$ 26. $\begin{cases} 2x - 3y = 14 \\ -x + 3y = -6 \end{cases}$

Connections

For Exercises 27–32, solve the equation. Check the solution.

27. $3x + 12 = 24$ 28. $-7x - 13 = 15$ 29. $8 - 2x = 30$

30. $-7 + 9x = 38$ 31. $-4 - 6x = -22$ 32. $8x + 17 = -15$

33. In parts (a)–(f), find the value of y when $x = -2$.

   a. $y = 3x - 7$ b. $3x - 2y = 10$ c. $7x - 4y = 12$

   d. $x = 4y - 2$ e. $3 = 2x - y$ f. $12 = -3x - 4y$

Notes _____

_____

_____

_____

Write an equation for the line satisfying the given conditions.

34. slope $= -4$, y-intercept $= 3$

35. slope $= \frac{2}{3}$, passing through the point $(3, 4)$

36. slope $= -\frac{3}{4}$, y-intercept $= 2$

37. passes through the points $(5, 4)$ and $(1, 7)$

For Exercises 38–43, identify the slope and y-intercept of the line.

38. $3x + 2y = 4$ **39.** $4x - 8y = 12$ **40.** $x - y = 7$

41. $y = 4x - 8$ **42.** $2y = 4x + 6$ **43.** $y = 9$

44. Two lines can intersect at 0 points (if they are parallel), 1 point, or an infinite number of points (if they are the same). In parts (a)–(d), give all the possible numbers of intersection points for the two figures. Make sketches to illustrate the possibilities.

a. a circle and a straight line   **b.** two circles

c. a circle and a triangle   **d.** a circle and a rectangle

45. A **chord** is a line segment joining two points on a circle. Segment AC in the diagram at the right is a chord.

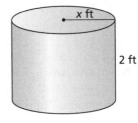

a. How many chords can be drawn by joining the labeled points on this circle?

b. How many points inside the circle are intersection points of two or more of the chords from part (a)?

c. The chords cut the circle into several non-overlapping regions. How many regions are formed?

46. Multiple Choice Which point is *not* on the graph of $2x - 5y = 13$?

A. $(9, 1)$ **B.** $(4, -1)$ **C.** $(0, 3.2)$ **D.** $(6.5, 0)$

47. The cylinder at the right represents an air conditioner unit with a radius of x feet and a height of 2 feet.

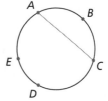

a. Draw a flat pattern for a cover for the air conditioner. (The top and sides need to be covered, but not the bottom.)

b. Which equation below represents the area of the cover? Which represents the volume? Justify your choices.

$y = 2\pi x^2$ $y = \pi x^2 + 4\pi x$

$y = 2x^3$ $y = \pi x(x + 4)$

Investigation 4 Solving Systems of Linear Equations   **61**

Notes _____

_____

_____

_____

48. Multiple Choice Kaya wants to fence off part of her yard for a garden. She has 150 feet of fencing. She wants a rectangular garden with a length 1.5 times its width. Which system represents these conditions?

F. $\begin{cases} 1.5w = \ell \\ w + \ell = 150 \end{cases}$ G. $\begin{cases} w = 1.5\ell \\ w + \ell = 150 \end{cases}$

H. $\begin{cases} 2w = 3\ell \\ w + \ell = 75 \end{cases}$ J. $\begin{cases} 3w = 2\ell \\ 2(w + \ell) = 150 \end{cases}$

49. Multiple Choice Which equation shows how to find one dimension of the garden described in Exercise 48?

A. $2.5w = 150$ B. $2.5\ell = 150$

C. $2w = 3(75 - w)$ D. $5w = 150$

50. This circle has a radius of 5 meters.

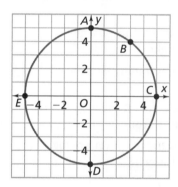

a. Copy and complete this table for the points on the circle.

	A	B	C	D	E
x	0	■	■	■	■
y	5	■	■	■	■

b. On grid paper, sketch the image of the circle after the rule $(x, y) \rightarrow (2x, 2y)$ is applied. Copy and complete this table for the images of points A, B, C, D, and E.

	A′	B′	C′	D′	E′
2x	0	■	■	■	■
2y	10	■	■	■	■

62   The Shapes of Algebra

Notes _____
_____
_____
_____

c. Sketch the image of the original circle after the rule $(x, y) \rightarrow (x + 2, y + 2)$ is applied. Copy and complete this table for the images of points A, B, C, D, and E.

	A'	B'	C'	D'	E'
$x + 2$	2	■	■	■	■
$y + 2$	7	■	■	■	■

d. Is the image in part (b) similar to or congruent to the original circle? What about the image in part (c)?

51. Without graphing, decide whether the graph of the equation is a line, a parabola, an exponential curve, an inverse variation curve, or a circle.

a. $2x - 3y = 10$ **b.** $x^2 + y^2 = 100$

c. $x^2 + x^2 = 100 - y$ **d.** $\frac{250}{x} = y$

e. $y = 2^x$ **f.** $y = x^2 - x^2 + x + 100$

g. $xy = 100$ **h.** $3x + 10 = y$

Tell whether the table represents a linear, quadratic, exponential, or inverse-variation relationship, and write an equation for the relationship.

52.

x	0	1	2	3	4	5	6	7
y	0	-3	-4	-3	0	5	12	21

53.

x	-1	0	1	2	3	4	5	6
y	$\frac{1}{3}$	1	3	9	27	81	243	729

54.

x	1	3	4	6	9	10	12	18
y	2	8	11	17	26	29	35	53

55.

x	1	2	3	4	6	8	10	12
y	12	6	4	3	2	1.5	1.2	1

Investigation 4 Solving Systems of Linear Equations   **63**

Notes

56. Tell which graph matches the equation.

    a. $y = 2^{x-1}$ **b.** $y = -x^2 + 2x + 8$ **c.** $y = (x + 2)(x - 4)$

    d. $y = 2^x$ **e.** $y = 2x^2$ **f.** $25 = x^2 + y^2$

Graph 1

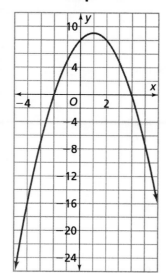

Graph 2

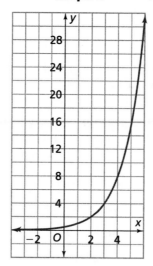

Graph 3

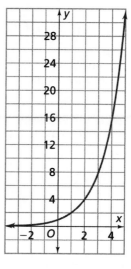

Graph 4

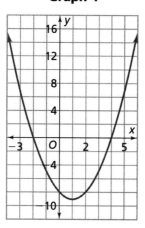

Graph 5

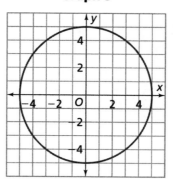

Graph 6

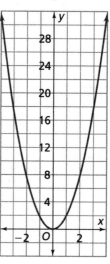

Notes _____

_____

_____

_____

Solve each equation for *x*.

57. $5(x + 4) - 2x = 5 + 6x + 2x$ **58.** $2(x + 2) - 6x = 6x + 8 - 2x$

59. $x^2 - 7x + 12 = 0$ **60.** $x^2 + 5x - 6 = 0$

Extensions

61. Yolanda and Marissa both babysit. Yolanda charges $5.50 an hour. Marissa charges a base rate of $20, plus $0.50 an hour.

   a. For each girl, write an equation showing how the charge depends on babysitting time.

   b. For what times are Marissa's charges less than Yolanda's?

   c. Is there a time for which Yolanda and Marissa charge the same amount?

62. Raj's age is 1 year less than twice Sarah's age. Toni's age is 2 years less than three times Sarah's age.

   a. Suppose Sarah's age is *s* years. What is Raj's age in terms of *s*?

   b. How old is Toni in terms of *s*?

   c. How old are Raj, Sarah, and Toni if the sum of their ages is 21?

63. Melissa and Trevor sell candy bars to raise money for a class field trip. Trevor sells 1 more than five times as many as Melissa sells. Together they sell 49 candy bars.

   a. Let *m* be the number of candy bars Melissa sells. Let *t* be the number of candy bars Trevor sells. Write a linear system to represent this situation.

   b. Solve your system to find the number of candy bars each student sells.

Notes _____

_____

_____

_____

64. Solve each system by using substitution or the combination method. You may get some strange results. In each case, graph the equations and explain what the puzzling results indicate about the solution.

a. $\begin{cases} x - 2y = 3 \\ -3x + 6y = -6 \end{cases}$

b. $\begin{cases} x - y = 4 \\ -x + y = -4 \end{cases}$

c. $\begin{cases} 2x - 3y = 4 \\ 4x - 6y = 7 \end{cases}$

d. $\begin{cases} 4x - 6y = 4 \\ -6x + 9y = -6 \end{cases}$

65. The equation of the line is $y = \frac{4}{3}x$. The equation of the circle is $x^2 + y^2 = 25$.

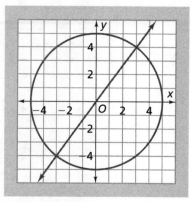

You can find the intersection points by solving the system below. Modify the substitution method to solve the system.

$\begin{cases} y = \frac{4}{3}x \\ x^2 + y^2 = 25 \end{cases}$

66. Write a system of the form $\begin{cases} ax + by = c \\ dx + ey = f \end{cases}$ that has the given solution.

a. $(3, 7)$ b. $(-2, 3)$ c. no solutions

66   The Shapes of Algebra

Notes _____

_____

_____

_____

67. Consider these equivalent systems.

$$\begin{cases} 2y - 3x = 0 \\ y + x = 75 \end{cases} \quad \text{and} \quad \begin{cases} 2y - 3x = 0 \\ 3y + 3x = 225 \end{cases}$$

a. Do the four equations in these two systems represent four different lines? Explain.

b. Adding the two equations in the second system gives $5y = 225$, or $y = 45$. Does $y = 45$ represent the same line as either equation in the system? Does it have anything in common with the lines in the system?

c. If you add the two equations in the first system, you get $3y - 2x = 75$. Does this equation represent the same line as either equation in the system? Does it have anything in common with the lines in the system?

d. What conjectures can you make about the results of adding any two linear equations? Consider the following questions:

- Will the result be a linear equation?
- Will the graph of the new equation have anything in common with the graphs of the original equation?

Notes _____

_____

_____

_____

Mathematical Reflections

4

In this investigation, you learned several strategies for finding solutions of systems of linear equations. These questions will help you summarize what you have learned.

Think about your answers to these questions. Discuss your ideas with other students and your teacher. Then write a summary of your findings in your notebook.

1. What is the goal in solving a system of linear equations such as the ones below?

$$\begin{cases} y = -3x + 5 \\ y = 4x - 8 \end{cases} \qquad \begin{cases} 3x + y = 5 \\ 2x + 5y = -8 \end{cases}$$

2. Tell which solutions strategy would be most efficient for the system. Give reasons for your choice.

   a. $\begin{cases} y = 4x - 5 \\ y = 1.5x + 8 \end{cases}$ **b.** $\begin{cases} x + 3y = 4 \\ x - 5y = 7 \end{cases}$

   c. $\begin{cases} 4x + 3y = 4 \\ x - 5y = 7 \end{cases}$ **d.** $\begin{cases} 4x + 3y = 4 \\ 2x - 5y = 7 \end{cases}$

3. How can you check a possible solution of a system of linear equations?

Notes _____

_____

_____

_____

Investigation 4

ACE
Assignment Choices

Differentiated Instruction
Solutions for All Learners

Problem 4.1
Core 1–7
Other 27–37, 61, and unassigned choices from previous problems

Problem 4.2
Core 8–14
Other 38–46, 62, and unassigned choices from previous problems

Problem 4.3
Core 15–20
Other 47–50, 63, and unassigned choices from previous problems

Problem 4.4
Core 21–26
Other 51–60, 64–67, and unassigned choices from previous problems

Adapted For suggestions about adapting Exercises 2–7 and other ACE exercises, see the CMP *Special Needs Handbook*.
Connecting to Prior Units 27–43, 46: *Moving Straight Ahead*; 46: *Variables and Patterns*; 47: *Filling and Wrapping*; 48, 49, 57–60: *Say It With Symbols*; 51–56: *Frogs, Fleas, and Painted Cubes; Growing, Growing, Growing; Thinking with Mathematical Models*

Applications

1. **a.** Matching equations to graphs: AD is represented by $y = -x + 5{,}500$
   BD is represented by $y = -0.5x + 3{,}250$
   BE is represented by $y = 0.2x + 2{,}200$
   CE is represented by $y = x - 1{,}000$
   b. AD intersects BE at $(2{,}750, 2{,}750)$
   AD intersects CE at $(3{,}250, 2{,}250)$
   BD intersects CE at $(2{,}833, 1{,}833)$

2. $(x, y) = (-3, -14)$ 3. $(x, y) = (7, 28)$

4. $(x, y) = (-2, -5)$ 5. $(x, y) = (-4, 20)$
6. $(x, y) = (10, 164)$ 7. $(y, y) = (\frac{29}{6}, -\frac{248}{3})$
8. $y = (-\frac{2}{3})x - 2$ 9. $y = (\frac{7}{9})x - \frac{4}{9}$
10. $y = -2x - 3$ 11. $y = (\frac{1}{4})x$
12. $y = x + 1$ 13. $y = -5x + 3$
14. $x = -1.5y - 3$
$\qquad x = (\frac{9}{7})y + \frac{4}{7}$
$\qquad x = -0.5y - 1.5$
$\qquad x = 4y$
$\qquad x = y - 1$
$\qquad x = -0.2y + 0.6$
15. $(x, y) = (3, 0)$
16. $(x, y) = (1.5, 0.5)$
17. $(x, y) = (-15, -22)$
18. $(x, y) = (1, 1)$
19. $(x, y) = (4, 2)$
20. $(x, y) = (1, 1)$
21. $(x, y) = (\frac{14}{3}, 1)$
22. $(x, y) = (2, -\frac{1}{9})$
23. $(x, y) = (-3, -2)$
24. $(x, y) = (-4, 2)$
25. $(x, y) = (-1.5, -3)$
26. One approach multiplies the second equation by 2 and then adds it to the first:

$$\begin{cases} 2x - 3y = 14 \\ -2x + 6y = -12 \end{cases}$$

$$3y = 2; \; y = \frac{2}{3}$$

$$2x - 3(\tfrac{2}{3}) = 14$$
$$2x = 16$$
$$x = 8$$
$$(x, y) = (8, \tfrac{2}{3})$$

(Or you could add both equations together to get $x = 8$ directly.)

Connections

27. $x = 4$ **28.** $x = -4$

29. $x = -11$ **30.** $x = 5$

31. $x = 3$ **32.** $x = -4$

33. a. $y = -13$ **b.** $y = -8$

   c. $y = -6.5$ **d.** $y = 0$

   e. $y = -7$ **f.** $y = -1.5$

34. $y = -4x + 3$ **35.** $y = (\frac{2}{3})x + 2$

36. $y = (-\frac{3}{4})x + 2$ **37.** $y = (-\frac{3}{4})x + \frac{31}{4}$

38. slope $= -1.5$; y-intercept $= 2$

39. slope $= 0.5$; y-intercept $= -1.5$

40. slope $= 1$; y-intercept $= -7$

41. slope $= 4$; y-intercept $= -8$

42. slope $= 2$; y-intercept $= 3$

43. slope $= 0$; y-intercept $= 9$

44. a. A line and a circle might intersect in 0, 1, or 2 points.

0 points   **1 point**   **2 points**

b. Two circles might intersect in 0, 1, 2, or infinitely many points (if they are identical).

0 points   **1 point**

2 points   **Infinite**

c. A circle and a triangle might intersect in 0, 1, 2, 3, 4, 5, or 6 points.

0 point   **1 point**   **2 points**

3 points   **4 point**   **5 points**   **6 points**

d. A circle and a rectangle might intersect in 0, 1, 2, 3, 4, 5, 6, 7, or 8 points.

0 point   **1 point**   **2 points**   **3 points**

4 points **5 points** **6 points** **7 points** **8 points**

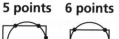

45. a. 10 (4 from each point, 5 points, but each chord counted twice)

   b. 5

   c. 16

46. C

47. a. One cover will look like this:

2πx ft

2 ft

x ft

b. Area is given by $\pi x^2 + 4\pi x$ and by $\pi x(x + 4)$; volume by $2\pi x^2$.

48. J   **49.** D

50. a. Coordinates of points on the circle.

	A	B	C	D	E
X	0	3	5	0	−5
Y	5	4	0	−5	0

b. New figure is a circle with radius 10 centered at origin.

	A′	B′	C′	D′	E′
2X	0	6	10	0	−10
2Y	10	8	0	−10	0

c. New figure is a circle with radius 5 centered at $(2, 2)$:

	A	B	C	D	E
X + 2	2	5	7	2	−3
Y + 2	7	6	2	−3	2

d. Circle in (b) is similar to original with scale factor 2; circle in (c) is congruent to the original.

51. a. Line

b. Circle

c. Parabola

d. Inverse variation curve

e. Exponential curve

f. Line; the x^2 terms cancel.

g. Inverse variation curve

h. Line

52. Quadratic; the second differences are a constant 2. The equation is $y = x(x - 4)$.

53. Exponential; the equation is $y = 3^x$.

54. Linear; the equation is $y = 3x - 1$.

55. Inverse variation; the product of each pair of x and y values is 12. The equation is $xy = 12$ or, equivalently, $\frac{12}{x} = y$ or $\frac{12}{y} = x$.

56. a. Graph 2   **b.** Graph 1
c. Graph 4   **d.** Graph 3
e. Graph 6   **f.** Graph 5

57. $x = 3$

58. $\frac{-1}{2} = x$

59. $x = 3$ or $x = 4$

60. $x = -6$ or $x = 1$

Extensions

61. a. Yolanda: $y = 5.5x$; Marissa: $y = 20 + 0.5x$

b. Marissa's rate is a better deal for the customer when $x > 4$ hours.

c. They have the same charge for $x = 4$ hours.

62. a. $R = 2s - 1$

b. $T = 3s - 2$

c. $S + (2S - 1) + (3S - 2) = 21$ when $S = 4$, $R = 7$ and $T = 10$.

63. a. $\begin{cases} m + t = 49 \\ 5t + 1 = m \end{cases}$

b. Trevor sold 41 and Melissa sold 8.

64. a. No solutions because the lines are disjoint and parallel; an algebraic solution: the system

$$\begin{cases} x - 2y = 3 \\ -3x + 6y = -6 \end{cases}$$

is equivalent to

$$\begin{cases} 3x - 6y = 9 \\ -3x + 6y = -6 \end{cases}$$

If $3x - 6y = 9$ and $-3x + 6y = -6$, then using the combination method: $(3x - 6y) + (-3x + 6y) = 9 + (-6)$, which leads to $0 = 3$. Since $0 = 3$ is a false statement there is no solution to this system.

b. Infinite solutions because the lines are identical; the algebraic solution for the system

$$\begin{cases} x - y = 4 \\ -x + y = -4 \end{cases}$$

If $x - y = 4$ and $-x + y = -4$, then using the combination method $(x - y) + (-x + y) = 4 + (-4)$ which leads to $0 = 0$. The solution of $0 = 0$ is a true statement and means that for all values (x, y) the equations in this system are equivalent.

c. No solutions because the lines are disjoint and parallel; An algebraic solution: the system is

$$\begin{cases} 2x - 3y = 4 \\ 4x - 6y = 7 \end{cases}$$

which is equivalent to

$$\begin{cases} 4x - 6y = 8 \\ 4x - 6y = 7 \end{cases}$$

If $4x - 6y = 8$ and $4x - 6y = 7$ then using the combination method: $4x - 6y - (4x - 6y) = 8 - 7$ which leads to $0 = 1$ which is a false statement so there is no solution to this system.

d. Infinite solutions because the lines are identical; an algebraic solution: the system

$$\begin{cases} 4x - 6y = 4 \\ -6x + 9y = -6 \end{cases}$$

is equivalent to

$$\begin{cases} 36x - 54y = 36 \\ -36x + 54y = -36 \end{cases}$$

(multiplying the first equation by 9 and the second equation by 6). If $36x - 54y = 36$ and $-36x + 54y = -36$, then using the combination method: $(36x - 54y) + (-36x + 54y) = 36 + (-36)$ which leads to $0 = 0$ which is a true statement and means that for all values (x, y) the equations in this system are equivalent.

65. Substituting $y = \frac{4}{3}x$ in the equation for

$$x^2 + \left(\tfrac{4}{3}x\right)^2 = 25$$
$$\tfrac{25}{9}x^2 = 25$$
$$x^2 = 9$$
$$x = \pm 3$$
$$x = 3 \text{ when } y = 4$$
$$x = -3 \text{ when } y = -4$$

66. Answers will vary. We suggest some strategies that can be used to generate the answers.

   a. Start with $x = 3$ and $y = 7$, then get something like $x + y = 10$ and $x - y = -4$, for example. You could also use $2x + 3y = 27$, etc.

   b. Same strategies as in (a) will work.

   c. Write one equation $ax + by = c$ and then another $ax + by = c + 1$, for example. Just make sure slopes of lines are the same, but intercepts are different.

67. a. No, the top two equations are exactly the same while the bottom two equations, when put into $y = mx + b$ form, are the same. Hence, the four equations represent only two distinct lines.

   b–c. It does not represent either equation in the system, but it passes through the point of intersection and hence provides the y-coordinate of the solution pair.

   d. The resulting equation will be linear since: $ax + by = c$ and $dx + ey = f$ together imply that $(a + d)x + (b + e)y = c + f$.

   The resulting equation will pass through the intersection of $ax + by = c$ and $dx + ey = f$ if such an intersection exists. If they are parallel, then the new equation will also be parallel.

Possible Answers to Mathematical Reflections

1. The goal in solving systems of linear equations like those shown is to find values of the unknowns x and y that satisfy both equations simultaneously. A solution to a system with two unknowns is either an ordered pair of numbers, no solution, or an infinite number of solutions.

2. In the given problems the most efficient strategy is likely to be:

   a. Setting $4x - 5 = 1.5x + 8$ and proceeding as in solving linear equations with one variable. When the value of x is known, substitute in either equation to find the corresponding value of x.

   b. Subtract one equation from the other to eliminate x. Then solve the resulting equation for y and substitute that value in either original equation to find the corresponding value of x. You could also solve both equations for x in terms of y, set the resulting expressions in y equal, and then solve for y.

   c. This system could be solved by solving the second equation for x in terms of y and then substituting that expression for x in the first equation.

   d. This system seems likely to be solved most easily by multiplying both sides of the second equation by 2 and then subtracting it from the first equation. This will eliminate x, providing an easy solution for y.

3. A proposed solution for a system of linear equations in two variables can be checked by substituting the numerical values for each unknown and determining whether the resulting statements are in fact equalities.

Investigation 5 Linear Inequalities

Mathematical and Problem-Solving Goals

- Solve linear inequalities in two variables
- Recognize differences between strict, $<$, and inclusive, $\leq$, inequalities
- Solve simple systems of linear inequalities

Work in Investigation 3 and Investigation 4 has set the students up to understand what it means to solve a system of linear inequalities. The purpose of this investigation is to give students a glimpse of the power and utility of linear inequalities. Many real-world statements can be translated into mathematical inequalities. For example, what someone spends on clothes and music and going to movies should be *no more than* her allowance.

Summary of Problems

Problem 5.1 Limiting Driving Miles

Uses two questions about the relationship between automobile mileage and air pollution to introduce the notion that the solution graph for a linear inequality in two variables will be a half-plane. It addresses the simplest case in which there is a single linear inequality of the form

$x + y \leq 1{,}000$. Students first plot possibilities for solutions of a linear inequality in two variables and then think about how to represent all possible answers.

Problem 5.2 Limiting Carbon Dioxide Emissions

Extends understanding of solutions and graphs for linear inequalities while introducing the notion of compound inequality conditions formed using "and" and "or." This sort of compound inequality condition is developed further in Problem 5.4.

Problem 5.3 Graphs of Linear Inequalities

Generalizes the notion of linear inequality to a variety of examples given in symbolic and graphic form, but without story context to limit the domains to positive values of the variables. It also gives students a chance to match inequalities and their graphs with a view toward developing strategies for graphing inequalities.

Problem 5.4 Systems of Linear Inequalities

Formalizes the notion of a system of linear inequalities and its graph.

	Suggested Pacing	Materials for Students	Materials for Teachers	ACE Assignments
All	5 days	graph paper		
5.1	1 day	Labsheet 5.1 (one per pair)	Transparencies 5.1A, 5.1B	1, 2, 13, 14
5.2	$1\frac{1}{2}$ days		Transparency 5.2	3, 4, 15
5.3	1 day		Transparencies 5.3 A–D	5–8
5.4	$1\frac{1}{2}$ days		Transparency 5.4	9–12, 16–20
MR	$\frac{1}{2}$ day			

Limiting Driving Miles

Goal

- Represent solutions to a simple linear inequality in two variables

Launch 5.1

This problem introduces students to simple inequalities by starting with a familiar problem situation. You might launch this problem by asking students to think about situations that can be modeled by inequalities.

The story used here to motivate thinking about inequalities is about a family that is trying to be environmentally responsible. They want to limit their car emissions as they drive their two family cars.

Describe the situation in Problem 5.1, and then pose the problem from Getting Ready. At first students may give answers like 600 miles on the car, 400 miles on the SUV, or 500 on each; that is, answers that sum to exactly 1,000. If students do not offer any possibilities that sum to less than 1,000, ask if 400 miles on the SUV and 400 miles on the car would be a reasonable possibility.

Show Transparency 5.1B. Ask students to plot the points that they suggested as possible answers to the Getting Ready.

Summarize discussion of the Getting Ready by indicating that the goal of the investigation is to develop some strategies for finding and representing solutions to inequalities.

Pair students up to think about how to represent all the possible answers.

Explore 5.1

After students have finished with Question A, check whether students recognize that any point in the region $x \geq 0, y \geq 0, x + y \leq 1,000$ is a possible answer to the inequality. Look for ways that the students choose to represent this region.

Summarize 5.1

Have groups display their graphical work and explain their thinking. Share with them the convention of shading the region of solutions. Ask why no solutions appear to the left of the vertical axis or to the bottom of the horizontal axis (because we are dealing with a practical situation in which the number of miles driven cannot be negative).

Suggested Questions

- *How do we know the point (400, 400) should be circled?* (Because $400 + 400 \leq 1,000$.)

- *How do we know all of these points in the shaded region are solutions?* (Because for all of them, the sum of the coordinates is less than or equal to 1,000.)

- *What about these points on the line* $x + y = 1000$? *Are they solutions?* (Yes, because the inequality is less than or equal to.)

- *What about the point (600, 600)? How do we know that should not be circled or shaded?* (Because $600 + 600 > 1,000$.)

- *How do we know that all of the points outside the shaded region are not solutions?* (Because the sum of the coordinates for any of those points is greater than 1,000.)

Have students check a few points outside the region to verify that the sum of their coordinates is greater than 1,000.

For Question B, ask students what other points are possibilities. Ask how they represented this on a graph. Some may have found that if they could darken every possible answer, the result would look like a shaded region.

Collect strategies for Question C. Some students may have graphed the line $x + y = 800$ and shaded in the triangular region bounded by $x + y \leq 800, x \geq 0, y \geq 0$.

For Question D, ask students to share the inequalities they wrote down to describe the situations in Questions A and C. Ideally, students will also include inequalities to represent the fact that miles driven cannot be negative. You may want to raise this point if students do not.

5.1 Limiting Driving Miles

Mathematical Goal

- Represent solutions to a simple linear inequality in two variables

Launch

Discuss the Getting Ready with students.

Ask students to plot the points that they suggested as possible answers to the Getting Ready on Transparency 5.1B.

Pair students up to think about how to represent all the possible answers.

Materials
- Transparencies 5.1A, 5.1B
- Labsheet 5.1 (1 per pair)

Explore

After students have finished with Question A, check whether students recognize that any point in the region $x \geq 0, y \geq 0, x + y \leq 1,000$ is (at least theoretically!) a possible answer to the inequality. Look for ways that the students choose to represent this.

Summarize

Have groups display their graphical work and explain their thinking. Share with them the convention of shading the region of solutions. Ask:

- *Why do no solutions appear to the left of the vertical axis or to the bottom of the horizontal axis?*

To emphasize that the shaded region is in fact the region of solutions, ask:

- *How do we know the point (400, 400) should be circled? How do we know all of these points in the shaded region are solutions?*
- *What about these points on the line* x + y = 1,000? *Are they solutions?*
- *What about the point (600, 600)? How do we know that should not be circled or shaded?*

Point to the unshaded region and ask:

- *How do we know that all of these points are not solutions?*

For Question B, ask:

- *What other points are possibilities? How did you represent this on a graph?*

Collect strategies for Question C.

For Question D, have students share the inequalities they wrote down to describe the situations in Questions A and C. Ideally, students will also include inequalities to represent the fact that miles driven cannot be negative.

Materials
- Student notebooks

ACE Assignment Guide for Problem 5.1

Core 1, 2, 13, 14

Other unassigned choices from previous problems

Adapted For suggestions about adapting Exercise 1 and other ACE exercises, see the CMP *Special Needs Handbook*.

Answers to Problem 5.1

A. Answers may vary. One possibility is shown here:

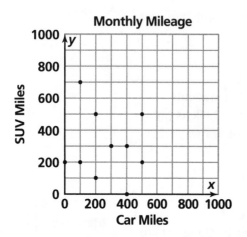

B. 1. Yes. Others are (100, 300), (700, 0), etc.

   2. Any point in the triangular region shown below is (theoretically at least!) a possibility.

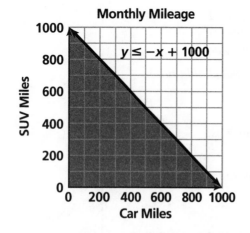

3. They are above and to the right of the line $y = -x + 1,000$.

C. 1.

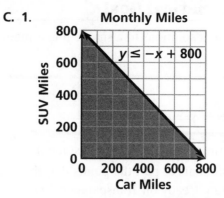

2. One possible answer: I graphed the line $x + y = 800$ and shaded the triangular region bounded by that line and the x- and y-axes.

D. For Question A, the inequalities are: $x + y \leq 1,000, x \geq 0, y \geq 0$. For Question B, the inequalities are: $x + y \leq 800, x \geq 0, y \geq 0$. Students may have chosen different letters to represent the axes, and they may not include the inequalities $x \geq 0, y \geq 0$. It's useful if students recognize that the axes are acting as bounds because of the situation.

5.2 Limiting Carbon Dioxide Emissions

Goal

- Develop skill in solving linear inequalities in two variables

Launch 5.2

This problem continues the story of Vince's family's work to make environmentally aware decisions. They have found out that their car emits an average of about 0.75 pounds of carbon dioxide per mile, and their SUV emits an average of 1.25 pounds per mile. Begin by asking the questions in the Getting Ready.

Suggested Questions

- *If Vince's family wants to limit emissions from their car to at most 600 pounds per month, how many miles could they drive their car?* (At most 800 miles.)

- *How do you know?* (One possible answer is an algebraic answer: $0.75x = 600$ yields $x = 800$ miles.)

- *If the family wants to limit emissions from their SUV to at most 600 pounds per month, how many miles could they drive their SUV?* (At most 480 miles.)

- *How do you know?* (One possible answer is an algebraic answer: $1.25x = 600$ yields $x = 480$ miles.)

- *Suppose they wanted to limit emissions from both vehicles to at most 600 pounds. What are some possibilities for miles they could drive each vehicle?* (There are lots of possibilities, including 300 miles on the car and 240 miles on the SUV, or 300 miles on the car and 100 miles on the SUV.)

Post enough possibilities from students so that it becomes clear that once again a graph would be a good way to represent the possibilities.

Have students work in pairs or small groups on Problem 5.2.

Explore 5.2

Check on students' progress to see how they are thinking about their solutions. In particular, see if students can correctly interpret Question B, parts (1) and (2) as problems that are similar to problems in Investigation 3. For Question B, parts (3) and (4), make sure that they can write the correct inequalities and represent the solutions graphically.

Summarize 5.2

Have students share their results on the tasks, explaining their reasoning as they work. For Question B, part (3), ask:

Suggested Questions

- *Why does this inequality (or set of inequalities, if they have included $0.75x + 1.25y \leq 600$, $x \geq 0, y \geq 0$) describe the set of possibilities?* (Because we need the total emissions from the car and the SUV to be at most 600 pounds. $0.75x$ represents the total emissions from the car, and $1.25y$ represents the total emissions from the SUV. The total from both is the sum $0.75x + 1.25y$. This is just like setting up a linear equation in two variables, but since we don't necessarily want exactly 600 pounds, we use an inequality.)

For Question B, part (4), ask:

- *Why does this graph represent the set of possibilities?* [For any point (x, y) in the shaded region, $0.75x + 1.25y$ is at most 600 pounds.]

Have students share solutions for question C.

5.2 Limiting Carbon Dioxide Emissions

Mathematical Goal

• Develop skill in solving linear inequalities in two variables

Launch

This problem continues the story of Vince's family's work to make environmentally aware decisions. They have found out that their car emits an average of about 0.75 pounds of carbon dioxide per mile, and their SUV emits an average of 1.25 pounds per mile.

Ask the questions in the Getting Ready.

• *If Vince's family wants to limit emissions from their car to at most 600 pounds per month, how many miles could they drive their car? How do you know?*

• *If the family wants to limit emissions from their SUV to at most 600 pounds per month, how many miles could they drive their SUV? How do you know?*

• *Suppose they wanted to limit emissions from both vehicles to at most 600 pounds. What are some possibilities for miles they could drive each vehicle?*

Have students work in pairs or small groups.

Materials
• Transparency 5.2

Explore

Check to see that students correctly interpret Question B, parts (1) and (2), as problems like those they saw in Investigation 3. For Question B, parts (3) and (4), make sure that they can write the correct inequalities and represent the solutions graphically.

Summarize

Have students share their results on the tasks, explaining their reasoning as they work. For Question B, part (3), ask:

• *Why does this inequality (or set of inequalities, if they have included $x \geq 0, y \geq 0$) describe the set of possibilities?*

For Question B, part (4), ask:

• *Why does this graph represent the set of possibilities?*

Have students share solutions for Question C.

Materials
• Student notebooks

ACE Assignment Guide for Problem 5.2

Differentiated Instruction
Solutions for All Learners

Core 3, 4

Other *Connections* 15; unassigned choices from previous problems

Adapted For suggestions about adapting ACE exercises, see the CMP *Special Needs Handbook*.

Answers to Problem 5.2

A. 1. (150, 390), (300, 300), (100, 420), (400, 240), (500, 180), (600, 120), etc.

2. $0.75x + 1.25y = 600$

3.

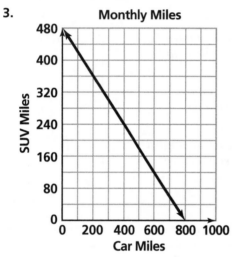

B. Using either the car or the SUV but not both.

1. $0.75x \leq 600$ (Here x is positive.)

2. $1.25y \leq 600$ (Here y is positive.)

3. $0.75x + 1.25y \leq 600$ (Here x and y are positive, so students may also write $x \geq 0$, $y \geq 0$.)

4.

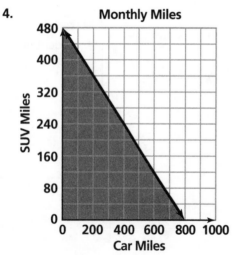

5. Any point in the triangular region shaded in part (4). This region is bounded by $x = 0$, by $y = 0$ and by $0.75x + 1.25y = 600$.

C. 1. $0.5x + 1.2y \leq 500$ (Here x and y are positive, so students may also write $x \geq 0$, $y \geq 0$.)

2.

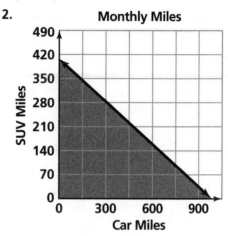

3. Any point in the triangular region indicated in part (a). This region is bounded by $x = 0$, $y = 0$ and by $0.5x + 1.2y = 500$.

Graphs of Linear Inequalities

Goals

- Develop skill at recognizing graphs of different inequalities

- Recognize differences between strict, $<$, and inclusive, $\leq$, inequalities

So far, all of the inequalities we have looked at have been in bounded regions of the plane. Further, all of our inequalities have been *inclusive* in the sense that we were looking at limiting carbon dioxide emissions to at most 600 pounds per month.

We have included a fair number of inequalities to match with graphs because our hope is that students will recognize that a linear inequality divides the plane into regions. Matching the regions with the inequalities is a matter of matching the associated equations and then the regions.

Launch 5.3

You might launch work on this problem by using the Getting Ready. Put up a transparency of the graph at the beginning of Problem 5.3.

Suggested Questions

- *How would the graph be different if Vince's family had wanted their carbon dioxide emissions to be at least 600 pounds per month?* (Instead of being bounded above by the line $0.75x + 1.25y = 600$, that line is a lower bound. The region looks like this:

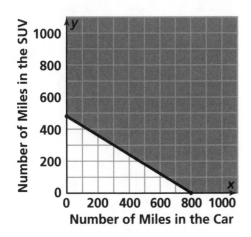

- *What are some possibilities for numbers of miles the family could drive their vehicles?* (Anything in that region—for example, they could drive each vehicle 1,000 miles.)

- *How would the graph be different if the family had wanted their carbon dixode emissions to be less than 600 pounds per month?* (We would not want to include the graph of the equation $0.75x + 1.25y = 600$, i.e., the line would not be part of the region.)

- *We sometimes draw the equation as a broken line, $- - - -$, to show that it is not included in the solution set.*

- *As you work on this problem, think about strategies for figuring out which graph matches which inequality. Test your strategies out!*

Have the students work in pairs for this problem.

Explore 5.3

As you circulate, listen to students' strategies for matching the graphs with the various inequalities. Note any difficulties and address them in the summary.

Summarize 5.3

Have students present their solutions and reasoning to the matching in Questions A and B. Listen to the strategies students used to match. One common strategy is to graph the boundary line and then choose a test point to identify which region of the plane is associated with the linear inequality and a point on the line to see if it is part of the inequality.

One thing that may come up for students is that they have graphed inequalities like $x \geq -3$ on a number line. From that perspective, "graph the inequality $x \geq -3$" is ambiguous; it means either graph on a number line or on an x-y plane. The situation is analogous to plotting the point $x = -3$ on a number line or graphing the line $x = -3$. That is, the context matters.

For Question C, some caution is in order. It's very useful to write the inequalities in either the form $y \leq mx + b$ or $y \geq mx + b$—but even this form requires care! The tendency with a form like $y \geq mx + b$ is to say, "we need the region where y is 'above' $mx + b$"—which is true, but "above" is not a very precise description. For example, look at the inequality $y - 3x \geq 6$. We can write this as $y \geq 3x + 6$.

The graph of this inequality is shown in Question A, choice (b). In cases like this, students often draw the graph with the other region shaded because it somehow looks to them like y is greater. Testing a point from each region should convince students that the graph associated with this inequality is indeed from Question A, choice (b).

Question D is simply a way of sharing the convention of drawing a dotted line for strict inequalities.

5.3 Graphs of Linear Inequalities

Mathematical Goals

- Develop skill at recognizing graphs of different inequalities
- Recognize differences between strict, $<$, and inclusive, $\leq$, inequalities

Launch

Put up Transparency 5.3A.

- *How would the graph be different if Vince's family had wanted their carbon dioxide emissions to be at least 600 pounds per month?*

Put up Transparency 5.3B.

- *What are some possibilities for numbers of miles the family could drive their vehicles?*

- *How would the graph be different if the family had wanted their carbon dioxide emissions to be less than 600 pounds per month?*

- *As you work on this problem, think about strategies for figuring out which graph matches which inequality. Test your strategies out!*

Have the students work in pairs for this problem.

Materials
- Transparencies 5.3A–D

Explore

As you circulate, listen to students' strategies for matching the graphs with the various inequalities. Note any difficulties and address them in the summary.

Summarize

Have students present their solutions and reasoning to the matching in Questions A and B. One strategy is to graph the boundary line and then choose a test point to identify which region of the plane is associated with the linear inequality.

For Question C, it's useful to write the inequalities in either the form $y \leq mx + b$ or $y \geq mx + b$—but even this form requires care! The tendency with a form like $y \geq mx + b$ is to say, "We need the region where y is 'above' $mx + b$"—which is true, but "above" is not a very precise description. For example, look at the inequality $y - 3x \geq 6$. We can write this as $y \geq 3x + 6$.

The graph of this inequality is shown in choice b in Question A. In cases like this, students often draw the graph with the other region shaded because it somehow looks like y is greater. Testing a point from each region should convince students that the graph associated with this inequality is indeed graph b.

Use Transparency 5.3D to discuss Question D, which illustrates a graph of a strictly less-than case.

Materials
- Student notebooks

ACE Assignment Guide for Problem 5.3

Differentiated Instruction
Solutions for All Learners

Core 5–8

Other unassigned choices from previous problems

Adapted For suggestions about adapting ACE exercises, see the CMP *Special Needs Handbook*.

Answers to Problem 5.3

A. Matching the inequalities with the graphs.

1. b   **2.** d   **3.** c   **4.** a

5. e   **6.** g   **7.** f   **8.** h

B. Answers may vary. One possibility is to graph the equation associated with the inequality and then check test points.

C. Rewriting inequalities.

1. $y \geq 6 + 3x; y \leq \frac{x}{3} - 2; y \leq 6 - 3x;$
$y \leq -\frac{x}{3} + 2$

2. This way of writing the inequalities may make the graphs easier to identify because we can more easily identify the boundaries and possibly which region of the plane is the region of solution.

D. Strict inequality.

1. No, because $12 = 6 + 6$. We are looking for a strict inequality.

2. The solutions to the equation $y = 3x + 6$ are not solutions to the inequality $y < 3x + 6$ because the inequality is strict. Therefore the line is dotted/dashed.

5.4 Systems of Linear Inequalities

Goal

- Solve simple systems of linear inequalities

The previous work in this investigation and in Investigation 4 sets students up to be able to think about graphical methods for finding solutions to systems of linear inequalities. In previous problems we have been working with one constraint. In this problem, we introduce a second constraint.

Launch 5.4

Once again, Vince's family is trying to be environmentally aware. By this time, students may be wondering why they have an SUV at all, since they are trying to make good environmental choices, and the SUV is clearly harder on the environment. We find out that the Mertzes have a dog named Chance who likes to go on trips with them, and when they take him along, they drive the SUV.

Suggested Questions

- *The family drives their SUV more than twice as many miles as their car because they like to take their dog, Chance, along with them. What inequality expresses this situation?*
  ($s > 2c$, where s represents the number of miles they plan to drive the SUV and c represents the number of miles they plan to drive the car.)

- *Why does this inequality represent the situation?* (Because the number of miles in the SUV is at least twice the number of miles in the car.)

- *They also want to maintain their commitment to the environment by sticking to their plan of limiting carbon dioxide emissions to less than 600 pounds per month. The set of inequalities:*
  s > 2c
  0.75c + 1.25s < 600
  is called a system of inequalities. Why might we write this? (Because we want solutions to both inequalities simultaneously.)

- *What does each part of this system of inequalities represent?* (s is the number of miles the SUV is driven, $2c$ is twice the number of miles the car is driven, 0.75 is the number of pounds of CO_2 emitted per mile of car driving, 1.25 is the number of pounds of CO_2 emitted per mile of SUV driving, and 600 is the maximum amount of monthly emissions the family is willing to make.)

- *Why does this system represent the situation?* (Because both the components of the situation are taken into account.)

Note that s and c are both positive again, so we could also write this system:

$$s > 2c$$
$$0.75c + 1.25s < 600$$
$$x \geq 0, y \geq 0$$

In this problem, students will work on solving this system of linear inequalities by graphing. Arrange the students in groups of two or three.

Explore 5.4

Students should work on graphing the two different inequalities on the same axis. Give them some time to think about what the different regions of their graphs represent. In particular, they should realize that in order to be in the solution set of the system, a region must be in the solution set of each inequality in a system. Ask some groups to put their graphs for Question A on a transparency for use in the summary.

INVESTIGATION 5

Summarize 5.4

Have students present their solutions and explanations to Question A, parts (1) and (2). When a good graph is on the overhead, ask students to describe what each region of the graph represents—not just the region of solution.

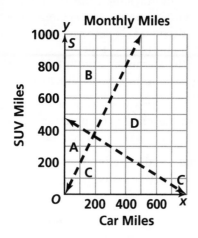

Monthly Miles

On the student's graph, label each region as shown.

Suggested Questions

- *What do points in region A represent?* (They represent solutions to both inequalities. These points are pairs of distances that result in less than 600 pounds of emissions and more than twice as many SUV miles as car miles.)

- *What do points in region B represent?* (Points that are solutions to the inequality $s > 2c$ and not $0.75c + 1.25s < 600$. In other words, these are the possibilities for miles that the family drives their SUV more than twice as much as their car where their emissions are more than 600 pounds per year.)

- *What do points in region C represent?* (This is the set of points that are solutions to $0.75c + 1.25s < 600$ but not $s > 2c$. In other words, the family is limiting their emissions, but they are driving their SUV less than twice the miles that they are driving their car.)

- *What do points in region D represent?* (This is the set of points that are solutions to neither inequality. The family is driving their SUV less than twice as much as they are driving their car, and their total emissions is more than 600 pounds per month.)

Having done this together, go over the students' solutions to Question B. Repeat some of the questions above.

5.4 Systems of Linear Inequalities

Mathematical Goal

- Solve simple systems of linear inequalities

Launch

Once again, Vince's family is trying to be environmentally aware. By this time, students may be wondering why they have an SUV at all, since they are trying to make good environmental choices, and the SUV is clearly harder on the environment.

- *We find out that the family has a dog named Chance who likes to go on trips with them, and when they take him along, they drive the SUV.*

- *The family drives their SUV more than twice as many miles as their car because they like to take their dog, Chance, along with them.*

- *What inequality expresses this situation? Why does this inequality represent the situation?*

- *They also want to maintain their commitment to the environment by sticking to their plan of limiting carbon dioxide emissions to less than 600 pounds per month. The set of inequalities:*
  s > 2c
  0.75c + 1.25s < 600
  is called a system of inequalities. Why might we write this? What does each part of this system represent?

- *Note that* s *and* c *are both positive again, so we could also write this system:*
  s > 2c
  0.75c + 1.25s < 600
  x ≥ 0, y ≥ 0

Arrange the students in groups of two or three.

Materials
- Transparency 5.4

Explore

Students should work on graphing the two different inequalities on the same axis. Give them some time to think about what the different regions of their graphs represent. In particular, they should realize that in order to be in the solution set of the system, a region must be in the solution set of each inequality in a system.

Summarize

Have students present their solutions and explanations to Question A. When a good graph is on the overhead, ask students to describe what each region of the graph represents—not just the region of solution. To do this, label the four regions A–D.

Materials
- Student notebooks

continued on next page

Summarize
continued

 • *What do points in region A represent? In region B? In region C? Region D?*

Put up Transparency 5.4 to discuss Question B. Ask what the points in regions A–D represent.

ACE Assignment Guide for Problem 5.4

Core 9–12
Other *Connections* 16–18; *Extensions* 19–20; unassigned choices from previous problems

Adapted For suggestions about adapting ACE exercises, see the CMP *Special Needs Handbook*.
Connecting to Prior Units 12: *Shapes and Designs*

Answers to Problem 5.4

A. Graphing linear inequalities together to graph solutions to a system of linear inequalities.

1.

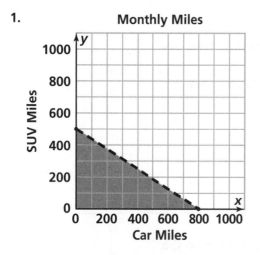

2.

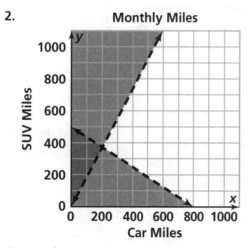

3. The set of points that is shaded in both inequalities is the solution set to both. For example, the point (100, 300) satisfies both inequalities, and it is in the region of overlap of the shaded areas.

B. 1. Region C is made up of points that are solutions to both inequalities. Region D is made of points in the solution set of $s \leq \frac{1}{3}c$, but not solutions of $0.75c + 1.25s \leq 400$. These points represent possibilities for numbers of miles on the car and SUV so that Nancy drives her car more than three times as much as her SUV, but her monthly emissions are greater than 400 pounds. Region A represents points in the solution set of $0.75c + 1.25s \leq 400$, but not $s \leq \frac{1}{3}c$. These points represent numbers of miles on her car and SUV so that her emissions are less than 400 pounds per month, but she puts less than three times the number of miles on her car that she puts on her SUV. Region B is made up of points that are solutions to neither inequality—so her emissions are more than 400 pounds and she puts less than three times the number of miles on her car that she puts on her SUV.

2. Region C

Note: An interesting question that could be asked is, "Do the points on the boundary of region C lie in the solution set for the problem?" Since this time the inequalities include the possibility that $s = \frac{1}{3}c$ and $0.75c + 1.25s = 400$, the boundary of region C also includes points in the solution set.

Investigation 5

Linear Inequalities

You have studied many relationships that can be modeled by linear equations. The points that satisfy such relationships fall on a straight line. Points that do not satisfy a linear relationship (do not fall on a line) satisfy a *linear inequality*.

Graphing helps make sense of how solutions to inequalities are related to what you know about solutions to linear equations. The situations in this investigation can be modeled by linear inequalities.

5.1 Limiting Driving Miles

Vince reads that cars are a major source of air pollution. He decides to look at his family's driving habits. They have two vehicles, a car and an SUV. His parents estimate that the family drives about 1,200 miles each month. They decide to try to limit their driving to no more than 1,000 miles each month.

Investigation 5 Linear Inequalities   **69**

Notes _____

_____

_____

_____

- Find ten possible (*car miles, SUV miles*) pairs that give a total of no more than 1,000 miles.

- One month the family drove the car 500 miles and the SUV 500 miles. Was the total for this month "no more than" 1,000 miles?

Problem 5.1 Graphing "No More Than" Situations

A. On a copy of the grid at the right, plot the ten points you found in the Getting Ready.

B. Look at the pattern of plotted points.

   1. Are there other possible (*car miles, SUV miles*) pairs that give a total of no more than 1,000 miles?

   2. We refer to a part of a graph or plane as a *region*. Describe where the points are located that represent a total of no more than 1,000 miles.

   3. In what region are the points that do not meet this condition located? Give some examples of such points.

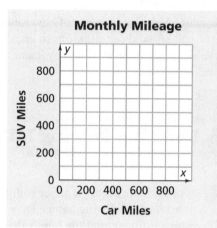

C. Suppose Vince's family wants to limit their driving to at most 800 miles per month.

   1. Draw a graph of (*car miles, SUV miles*) pairs that meet this condition.

   2. Describe the region of the graph that includes all points that represent a total of no more than 800 miles.

D. Write inequalities to model the situations in Questions B and C.

ACE Homework starts on page 78.

---

70   The Shapes of Algebra

Notes _____

_____

_____

_____

Vince finds out that his family's car emits an average of 0.75 pounds of carbon dioxide (CO_2) per mile. The SUV emits an average of 1.25 pounds of CO_2 per mile.

Getting Ready for Problem 5.2

- Suppose Vince's family wants to limit CO_2 emissions from their car to at most 600 pounds per month. How many miles could they drive their car?

- Suppose Vince's family wants to limit CO_2 emissions from their SUV to at most 600 pounds per month. How many miles could they drive their SUV?

- Suppose they want to limit the total CO_2 emissions from *both* vehicles to at most 600 pounds per month. What are some (*car miles, SUV miles*) pairs that allow them to meet this condition?

Investigation 5 Linear Inequalities **71**

STUDENT PAGE

Notes _____

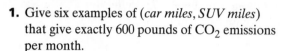

Problem 5.2 Solving Linear Inequalities by Graphing

A. Suppose Vince's family wants their total CO_2 emissions to be *exactly* 600 pounds per month.

   1. Give six examples of (*car miles, SUV miles*) that give exactly 600 pounds of CO_2 emissions per month.

   2. Write an equation to model this condition.

   3. Graph your equation.

B. Suppose the family wants to limit their total CO_2 emissions to *at most* 600 pounds per month.

   1. Write an inequality that describes the possibilities for the miles they can drive their car if they do not drive their SUV at all.

   2. Write an inequality that describes the possibilities for the miles they can drive their SUV if they do not drive their car at all.

   3. Write an inequality that describes the possibilities for how many miles they can drive their car *and* their SUV.

   4. Draw a graph displaying (*car miles, SUV miles*) pairs that satisfy the inequality you wrote in Question B, part (3).

   5. Describe the region of the graph that includes all points that represent a total of no more than 600 pounds of CO_2 emissions.

C. Soo's family has a minivan and a hybrid car. The minivan emits 1.2 pounds of CO_2 per mile. The car emits 0.5 pounds of CO_2 per mile. The family wants to limit their total emissions to at most 500 pounds per month.

   1. The family plans to drive both vehicles. Write an inequality to describe the possibilities for how many miles they can drive each vehicle.

   2. Draw a graph displaying the (*car miles, minivan miles*) pairs that satisfy the inequality you wrote in Question C, part (1).

   3. Describe the region of the graph that includes all points that satisfy the condition.

   ACE Homework starts on page 78.

72   The Shapes of Algebra

Notes _____

_____

_____

_____

In the last problem, you graphed the (*car miles, SUV miles*) pairs that limited CO_2 emissions to *at most* 600 pounds. To make a correct graph, you also had to consider the fact that the numbers of miles cannot be negative. In other words, all the points are in the first quadrant.

Getting Ready for Problem 5.3

- How would the graph of the inequality from Problem 5.2 be different if Vince's family wanted their CO_2 emissions to be *at least* 600 pounds per month?

- How would the graph be different if they wanted to limit their CO_2 emissions to be *less than* 600 pounds per month?

- Is $(-100, 540)$ a possible solution pair if they want to limit their CO_2 emissions to exactly 600 pounds per month? Why or why not?

The inequalities in the next problem are not limited to the first quadrant. As you work on the problem, think about general strategies for graphing inequalities. Notice that shading is used in the graphs to indicate the region in which the points satisfying the inequality lie.

Investigation 5 Linear Inequalities   **73**

Notes _____

_____

_____

_____

Problem 5.3 Graphs of Linear Inequalities

A. Match each inequality with its graph.

1. $y - 3x \geq 6$

2. $x - 3y \geq 6$

3. $3x + y \leq 6$

4. $x + 3y \leq 6$

5. $y \geq -3x$

6. $y \leq -3x$

7. $x \geq -3$

8. $y \geq -3$

a.

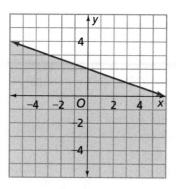

b.

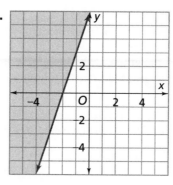

c.

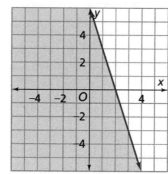

d.

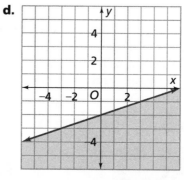

e.

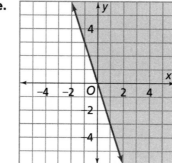

f.

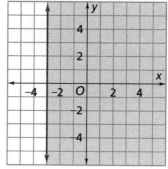

Notes _____

_____

_____

_____

g. 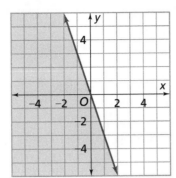 **h.**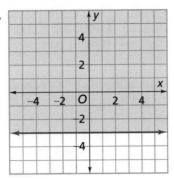

B. Describe your strategies for matching the graphs and inequalities.

C. 1. Rewrite the inequalities in parts (1)–(4) of Question A in either $y \leq mx + b$ or $y \geq mx + b$ form.

   2. Compare this form of the inequalities with their graphs. How might this form help you determine which regions should be shaded?

D. Think about the inequality $y < 3x + 6$.

   1. Does the pair $(2, 12)$ satisfy the inequality? Explain.

   2. Below is the graph of $y < 3x + 6$. How is this graph different from the graphs in Question A? What is the reason for this difference?

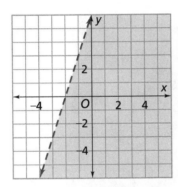

ACE **Homework starts on page 78.**

Investigation 5 Linear Inequalities   **75**

Notes _____

_____

_____

_____

Vince's family determines that, on average, they drive their SUV more than twice as many miles as they drive their car. Vince writes

$$s > 2c$$

where s represents the number of miles they drive the SUV, and c represents the number of miles they drive the car.

Why does this inequality represent the situation?

The family agrees to limit the total CO_2 emissions to less than 600 pounds per month. Recalling that the car emits 0.75 pounds of CO_2 per mile and the SUV emits 1.25 pounds of CO_2 per mile, Vince writes

$$0.75c + 1.25s < 600$$

Together, the two inequalities form a **system of linear inequalities.**

$$\begin{cases} s > 2c \\ 0.75c + 1.25s < 600 \end{cases}$$

Why does this system of linear inequalities describe the situation?

How would the system change if Vince's family agrees to total emissions that are at most *600 pounds rather than* less than *600 pounds?*

Notes _____

_____

_____

_____

A. 1. Graph the inequality $0.75c + 1.25s < 600$. This graph shows the possible (*car miles, SUV miles*) pairs for which the total CO_2 emissions are less than 600 pounds per month.

2. On the same axis, graph the inequality $s > 2c$. This graph shows the possible (*car miles, SUV miles*) pairs for which the number of SUV miles is more than twice the number of car miles.

3. Where on the grid are the points that satisfy both conditions?

B. Nancy has a car and an SUV with the same emissions as Vince's family's vehicles. She will drive her car at least three times as much as her SUV. She wants to limit the total CO_2 emissions to at most 400 pounds per month. She draws the following graph.

Limiting CO$_2$ Emissions

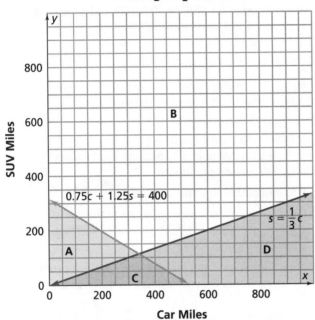

1. Describe what information the points in each region represent in terms of the situation.

2. In which region(s) are the points that satisfy both conditions?

ACE **Homework starts on page 78.**

STUDENT PAGE

Notes _____

_____

_____

_____

(77) 116

Applications

1. Ana has a car and a motorcycle. She wants to limit the combined mileage of the two vehicles to at most 500 miles per month.

   a. Write an inequality to model this condition.

   b. Draw a graph of all the (*car miles, motorcycle miles*) pairs that satisfy this condition.

   c. What strategy did you use to draw your graph?

2. A developer plans to build housing for at least 50 families. He wants to build some single-family houses and some four-family apartment buildings.

   a. Write an inequality to model this situation.

   b. Draw a graph to display the possible pairs of numbers of single-family houses and apartments the developer can build.

3. The Simon family's car emits 0.75 pounds of CO_2 per mile. Their minivan emits 1.2 pounds of CO_2 per mile. The Simons want to limit their emissions to at most 400 pounds per month.

   a. Write an inequality to model this condition.

   b. Draw a graph of all the (*car miles, minivan miles*) pairs that satisfy this condition.

4. Math Club members are selling games and puzzles. They make a profit of $10 on a game and $8 on a puzzle. They would like to make at least $200.

   a. What are some possibilities for the number of games and puzzles the Math Club can sell to reach its goal?

   b. Write an inequality to model this situation.

   c. Draw a graph of all the (*number of games, number of puzzles*) pairs that meet the goal.

For Exercises 5–7, find three (x, y) pairs that satisfy the inequality and three (x, y) pairs that do not. Then, draw a graph showing all the solutions.

   5. $x - 4y \geq 8$　　　　**6.** $4x - y \leq 8$　　　　**7.** $x - 4y < 8$

78　　The Shapes of Algebra

Notes _____

_____

_____

_____

8. In parts (a)–(d), graph the inequality.

   a. $x \geq 8 + 4y$ **b.** $x \geq 4$ **c.** $y < -2$ **d.** $2x - 4y \geq 8$

   e. What strategies did you use to draw the graphs?

9. Math Club members want to advertise their fundraiser each week in the school paper. They know that a front-page ad is more effective than an ad inside the paper. They have a $30 advertising budget. It costs $2 for each front-page ad and $1 for each inside-page ad. The club wants to advertise at least 20 times.

Homework Help Online
PHSchool.com
For: Help with Exercise 9
Web Code: ape-7509

   a. What are some possibilities for the numbers of front-page ads and inside-page ads the club can place?

   b. Write a system of linear inequalities to model this situation.

   c. Graph your system of inequalities. Be sure it is clear which region shows the solution.

10. The science club can spend at most $400 on a field trip to a dinosaur exhibit. It has enough chaperones to allow at most 100 students to go on the trip. The exhibit costs $3.00 for students 12 years and under and $6.00 for students over 12.

   a. How many students 12 years and under can go if no students over 12 go?

   b. How many students over 12 can go if no students 12 or under go?

   c. Write a system of linear inequalities to model this situation.

   d. Graph your system of inequalities. Be sure it is clear which region shows the solution.

Find three (x, y) pairs that satisfy the system of inequalities and three (x, y) pairs that do not. Then, draw a graph showing all the solutions.

11. $\begin{cases} 4x + 6y \leq 24 \\ x + 5y \leq 10 \end{cases}$ **12.** $\begin{cases} 2x - y \leq 4 \\ -x + y > -1 \end{cases}$

STUDENT PAGE

Notes _____

_____

_____

_____

Connections

For Exercises 13 and 14, use a graph to solve the system of equations.

13. $\begin{cases} x + y = 18 \\ 3x - y = 10 \end{cases}$

14. $\begin{cases} 80x + 40y = 400 \\ 20x + 80y = 420 \end{cases}$

Go Online
PHSchool.com
For: Multiple-Choice Skills Practice
Web Code: apa-7554

15. **Multiple Choice** What is the greatest whole-number value of x for which $4x < 14$?

   A. 11   **B.** 3   **C.** 4   **D.** 14

16. The parks commission in the town of Euclid decides to build a triangular park with one side that is 400 feet long.

   a. What are some possibilities for the lengths of the other sides? Explain.

   b. The city planner writes these inequalities.

   $$x + y > 400 \qquad x + 400 > y \qquad y + 400 > x$$

   The variables x and y represent possible lengths for the other two sides of the triangle. Why do these inequalities make sense? Why does the planner need all three inequalities to describe the situation?

   c. Graph the three inequalities from part (b) on the same axes. Describe the region that represents the possible lengths for the other sides of the park.

   d. Give a pair of lengths for the other two sides of the park. Explain how to find this answer by using your graph in part (c).

   e. Give a possible pair of lengths that could not be the other two side lengths. Explain how to find this answer using your graph in part (c).

17. Robin wants to make a smoothie out of milk, strawberry yogurt, and ice. She finds this nutrition information:

   - A cup of yogurt has 190 calories and 13 grams of protein.
   - A cup of milk has 100 calories and 9 grams of protein.
   - Ice has no calories and no protein.

   Robin wants her smoothie to have about 335 calories and 24 grams of protein.

   a. Write a system of equations to model the conditions for Robin's smoothie.

80 The Shapes of Algebra

Notes _____

_____

_____

_____

b. Graph the equations from part (a).

c. How much yogurt and milk should Robin use to make her smoothie? Explain.

18. Kadian also wants a milk-and-yogurt smoothie. She wants her smoothie to have *at most* 400 calories and *at least* 20 grams of protein.

a. Write a system of inequalities to model the conditions for Kadian's smoothie.

b. Graph the system of inequalities. Be sure it is clear which region shows the solution.

c. Use your graph for part (b) to describe some combinations of milk and yogurt amounts Kadian could use for her smoothie.

Extensions

19. Carolina wants to make a smoothie out of milk, strawberry yogurt, and ice. (See the protein and calorie information in Exercise 17.) She finds this additional information:

- A cup of milk has 306 milligrams of calcium.
- A cup of yogurt has 415 milligrams of calcium.
- Ice has no calcium.

She wants her smoothie to have at most 400 calories, at least 20 grams of protein, and at least 700 mg of calcium.

a. Write a system of inequalities to model the conditions for Carolina's smoothie.

b. Graph the system of inequalities. Be sure it is clear which region shows the solution.

c. What are some (*milk, yogurt*) combinations Carolina might choose?

20. Suppose you are making a smoothie. What nutrients are important to you? Would you like your smoothie to be a good source of vitamin C, calcium, fiber, protein, or calories? What ingredients would you like in your smoothie? Create guidelines for your smoothie. Using nutritional information about the ingredients, write a system of inequalities to help you decide how much of each item to include.

STUDENT PAGE

STUDENT PAGE

Notes _____

_____

_____

_____

Mathematical Reflections 5

In this investigation, you explored situations that could be modeled with linear inequalities. You also solved systems of linear inequalities to find values that satisfied several conditions. These questions will help you to summarize what you have learned.

Think about your answers to these questions. Discuss your ideas with other students and your teacher. Then write a summary of your findings in your notebook.

1. Suppose you are given one linear inequality. How can you use a graph to find solutions to the inequality?

2. Suppose you are given a system of linear inequalities. How can you use graphs to find solutions to the system of inequalities?

Notes _____

_____

_____

_____

Investigation 5

ACE
Assignment Choices

Differentiated Instruction
Solutions for All Learners

Problem 5.1
Core 1, 2, 13, 14
Other unassigned choices from previous problems

Problem 5.2
Core 3, 4
Other 15; unassigned choices from previous problems

Problem 5.3
Core 5–8
Other unassigned choices from previous problems

Problem 5.4
Core 9–12
Other 16–20; unassigned choices from previous problems
Connecting 16: *Shapes and Designs*

Adapted For suggestions about adapting Exercise 1 and other ACE exercises, see the CMP *Special Needs Handbook*.
Connecting to Prior Units 16: *Shapes and Designs*

Applications

1. a. Let x be the number of miles on the car and y be the number of miles on the motorcycle. Then the inequality is $x + y \leq 500$. Students may include $x \geq 0, y \geq 0$.

b.

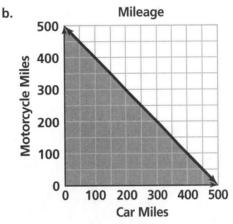

c. Answers may vary. One possibility: first, I drew the line x + y = 500. Then I shaded the region of solutions.

2. a. Let x be the number of single-family houses and y be the number of four-family apartment buildings. Then the inequality is $x + 4y \geq 50$. Students may include $x \geq 0$, $y \geq 0$.

b.

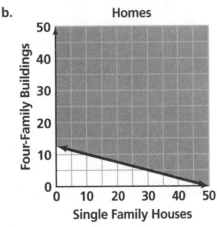

3. a. $0.75x + 1.2y \leq 400$

b.

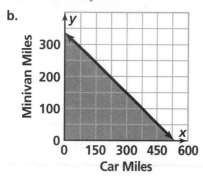

4. a. Answers may vary. Some possibilities: 20 games and 5 puzzles. 10 games and 16 puzzles.

b. Let g be the number of games the math club sells and p be the number of puzzles they sell. Then the inequality is $10g + 8p \geq 200$.

c.

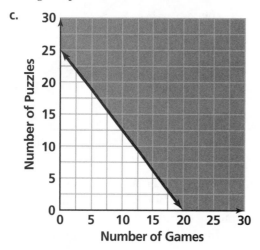

5. Answers will vary. Possible answers include $(10, 0)$, $(32, 2)$, and $(8, 0)$.

Answers will vary. Possible answers include $(10, 1)$, $(20, 5)$, and $(0, -1)$.

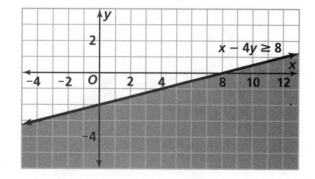

6. Answers will vary. Possible answers include $(0, 0)$, $(1, 2)$, $(2, 8)$.

Answers will vary. Possible answers include $(0, -10)$, $(2, -1)$, $(3, 3)$.

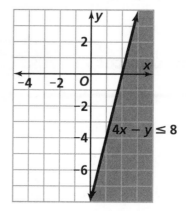

7. Answers will vary. Possible answers include $(0, 0)$, $(1, 2)$, $(2, 8)$.

Answers will vary. Possible answers include $(8, 0)$, $(16, 2)$, $(4, -1)$.

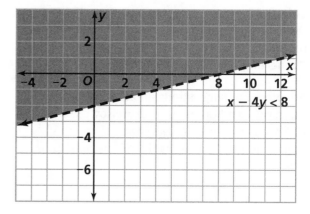

8. a.

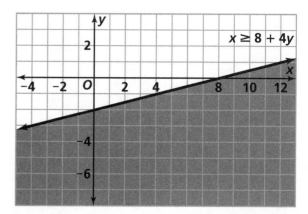

b.

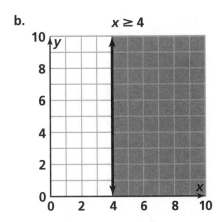

$x \geq 4$

c.

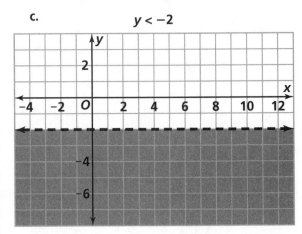

$y < -2$

d.

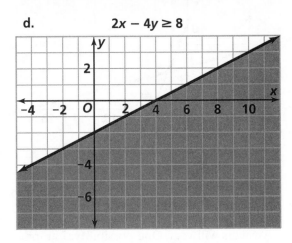

$2x - 4y \geq 8$

e. Answers will vary. One possible answer: I drew the line first, then decided whether or not it should be dotted. Then I chose test points to decide on which side of the line to shade.

9. a. Answers may vary, but they can advertise 20 times inside the paper and 5 times on the front page; or they can advertise 10 times on the front page and 10 times inside the paper; or they can advertise 30 times on the inside of the paper and never on the front page.

b. Let f be the number of times they advertise on the front page and let p be the number of times they advertise inside the paper. We know $f \geq 0$ and $p \geq 0$. Also:

$$2f + p \leq 30$$
$$f + p \geq 20$$

c.

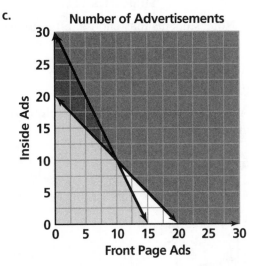

Number of Advertisements

Note that students may choose different axes for their graphs.

10. a. If no students older than 12 go on the trip, then as many as 100 students can go. This is within the budget of $400, and they are limited by the number of chaperones.

b. If no students 12 or younger go, then 66 students can go. This is because they are limited by the $400 budget.

c. Let x be the number of students 12 and younger going on the trip. Let y be the number of students older than 12 going on the trip. Then $x \geq 0$ and $y \geq 0$. Also:

$$3x + 6y \leq 400$$
$$x + y \leq 100$$

d.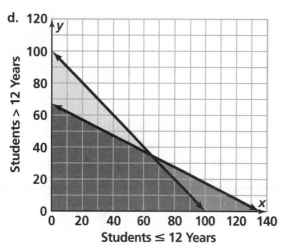

Note: students may choose different axes for their graphs.

11. Answers will vary. Possible solutions include $(0, 0), (1, 1), (-1, -1)$.

Answers will vary. Possible non-solutions include $(1, 2), (2, 4), (3, 6)$.

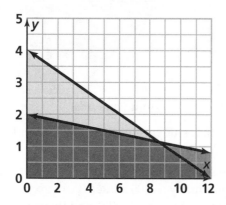

12. Answers will vary. Possible solutions include $(0, 3), (-1, 1), (-2, 0)$.

Answers will vary. Possible non-solutions include $(3, 0), (0, -2), (1, -3)$.

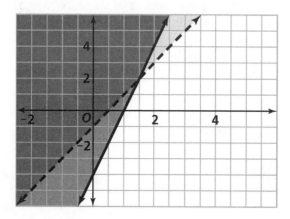

Connections

13. The solution is $(7, 11)$.

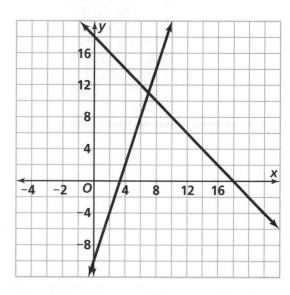

14. Possible estimate for solution: $(2.7, 4.6)$. Students can use trace or table features of their graphing calculators.

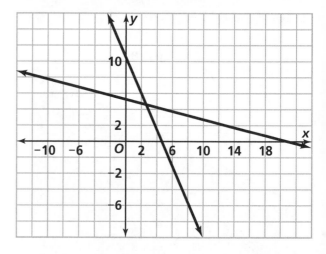

Answers will vary. One possibility: I graphed the equations of the lines and looked for the point of intersection.

15. B

16. a. Some possibilities for the lengths of the other side are 300 and 300, or 200 and 500. We know that the sum of any two sides must be greater than the third.

   b. The city planner needs all three inequalities because the sum of any of the two side lengths of a triangle must be greater than the third side.

c.

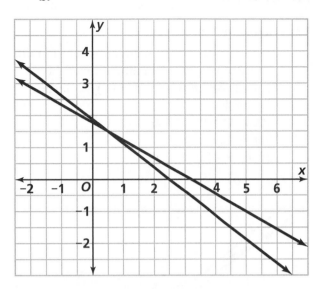

Answers describing the region that represents the possibilities will vary, but one possibility is that it looks like a rectangle that has been infinitely extended on one side.

d. Answers will vary. One possibility is (400, 100). You can see this in the graph because it's from the solution region for all three inequalities.

e. Answers will vary. One possible answer is (100, 100), because it is not in the solution region for all three inequalities.

17. a. Let m represent the number of cups of milk Robin uses and y stand for the number of cups of yogurt. Then the system of equations is:

$$100m + 190y = 335$$
$$9m + 13y = 24.$$

b.

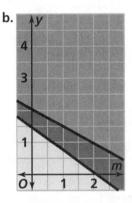

c. She needs to use half a cup of milk and 1.5 cups of yogurt, because the graphs of the two equations intersect where $m = 0.5$ and $y = 1.5$.

18. a. $\begin{cases} 100m + 190y \leq 400 \\ 9m + 13y \geq 20 \end{cases}$

b.

c. Some possibilities are 1 cup of milk and 1.5 cups of yogurt; or 0.7 cups of milk and 1.4 cups of yogurt; or a cup of yogurt and a cup of milk.

Extensions

19. systems with three inequalities

    a. Let m represent the number of cups of milk and y represent the number of cups of yogurt. We know $m \geq 0$ and $y \geq 0$. The system is

$$100m + 190y \leq 400$$
$$9m + 13y \geq 20$$
$$306m + 415y \geq 700$$

    b.

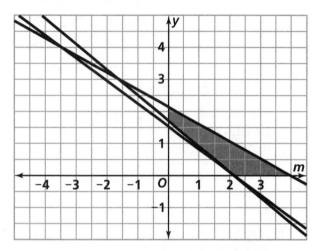

    c. Some possibilities are $(3, 0), (0, 2), (1.5, 1)$

20. Answers will vary.

Possible Answers to Mathematical Reflections

1. If the inequality has the form $ax + by \leq c$ or $ax + by \geq c$, first graph the equation $ax + by = c$, and then figure out which region represented the solution set of the inequality by testing points.

2. To find the solution to a system of linear inequalities, first find the regions of solution to each inequality and then find the intersection of those regions, which is the solution of the system.

Answers to Looking Back and Looking Ahead

1. a. The circle on the left has equation $(x + 3)^2 + y^2 = 25$; the circle on the right has the equation $(x - 3)^2 + y^2 = 25$. This can be confirmed by checking to see that particular points on each circle satisfy the equations. For example, $(-3, 5)$ satisfies the first equation and $(3, 5)$ satisfies the second equation.

This match of coordinate equations and geometric shapes is always counter-intuitive for students. They expect $(x - 3)^2 + y^2 = 25$ to be the one that represents a circle shifted to the left from the standard form centered at the origin. Full and convincing explanation of this translation idea is better left to a future course. The essential idea is that replacing x by $(x + 3)$ has the effect of making a point act like its counterpart 3 units to the right in the standard equation $x^2 + y^2 = 5^2$. Thus the image of this new circle will make it look as if the original has been shifted left 3 units.

b. The circles intersect at $(0, 4)$ and $(0, -4)$. The (x, y) coordinates of those points satisfy both equations: $(0 + 3)^2 + 4^2 = 25$ and $(0 - 3)^2 + (4)^2 = 25$ and $(0 - 3)^2 + (-4)^2 = 25$ and $(0 + 3)^2 + (-4)^2 = 25$.

c. $(-7 + 3)^2 + 3^2 = 25$

The next diagram shows a right triangle connecting the center of the circle to the point $(-7, 3)$. Using the Pythagorean theorem, we see that $4^2 + 3^2 = 5^2$.

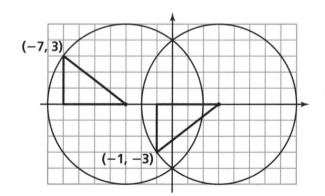

d. $(-1 - 3)^2 + (-3)^2 = 25$

See diagram for part (c). Using the Pythagorean theorem we see that $4^2 + 3^2 = 5^2$.

e. Interior of left circle is given by $(x + 3)^2 + y^2 < 25$; many possible points lie inside that circle. Each (x, y) pair can be checked by substitution.

Interior of right circle is given by $(x - 3)^2 + y^2 < 25$; many possible points lie inside that circle. Each (x, y) pair can be checked by substitution.

2. a. Slopes of the long sides are both $\frac{1}{2}$; slopes of the short sides are both -2.

b. The slopes of adjacent pairs of sides are such that $(\frac{1}{2})(-2) = -1$, the condition for perpendicularity of lines.

c. Midpoint coordinates are $(-1, 1.5)$, $(5, 2)$, $(1, -2.5)$, and $(-5, -3)$.

d. The figure formed is a parallelogram, a fact that can be confirmed by noting that the pairs of opposite sides have slopes $\frac{1}{12}$ and $\frac{9}{8}$, respectively.

3. a. One fairly natural way to write the system is
$$\begin{cases} 9x + 6y = 2{,}100 \\ x + y = 250 \end{cases}$$

b.

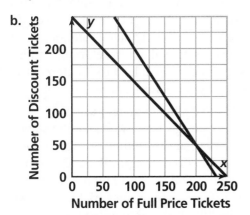

Number of Full Price Tickets

The solution suggested by the graph is $(200, 50)$, which means 200 full-price tickets and 50 discount tickets. This estimate is in fact the exact solution.

Check: $9(200) + 6(50) = 2{,}100$ and $200 + 50 = 250$.

Solutions by substitution may proceed like this:
$$y = 250 - x$$
$$9x + 6(250 - x) = 2{,}100$$
$$3x + 1{,}500 = 2{,}100$$
$$x = 200$$

$$200 + y = 250$$
$$y = 50$$

Here is one example of a way to use the linear combinations method to eliminate a variable:
$$(9x + 6y) - (9x + 9y) = 2{,}100 - 9(250)$$
$$-3y = -150$$
$$y = 50$$

$$x + 50 = 250$$
$$x = 200$$

4. a. One way to express the condition is $1.2x + 0.8y \geq 50$.

b. There are many possible pairs of values that satisfy the inequality in (b). For example, $1.2(30) + 0.8(20) = 52$.

The graph might look like this:

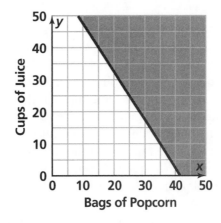

Bags of Popcorn

c. One way to express the investment constraint is $0.15x + 0.2y \leq 10$.

d. Once again, there are many possible ways to meet the constraint in (c). For example, $0.15(30) + 0.20(20) = 8.50$. The graph showing solutions of both constraints might look like this:

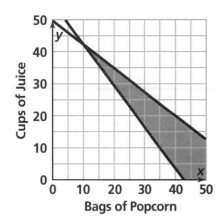

Explaining Your Reasoning

5. a. The coordinates of any point on a circle of radius r centered at the origin will satisfy the equation $x^2 + y^2 = r^2$.

   b. The coordinates of any point in the interior of a circle with radius r centered at the origin will satisfy the equation $x^2 + y^2 < r^2$.

6. a. To check whether the opposite sides of a polygon are parallel, we must first find the vertices of the polygon. Next, take the vertices of the endpoints of one side and find the slope of the line through these two endpoints. Compare this slope to the slope of the line through the endpoints of the side opposite this side. If the slopes are the same, then this pair of opposite sides is indeed parallel. Repeat for another pair of opposite sides in the polygon.

   b. To check whether the adjacent sides of a polygon are perpendicular, we proceed as before by finding the vertices of the polygon and calculating the slopes of the lines containing the endpoints of the adjacent sides under consideration. If we compare the slopes of these lines and find that they are negative reciprocals of one another, then they are perpendicular.

7. If we know the vertices to be points (x_1, y_1) and (x_2, y_2), then the midpoint of the segment with these as its endpoints is given by

$$\left(\frac{x_1 + x_2}{2}, \frac{y_1 + y_2}{2} \right)$$

8. a. Each graph will be a single straight line.

   b. The solutions will be all the points at which the lines intersect.

   c. There are three possible cases: The lines intersect in no points, and are thus parallel, in which case the system has no solution. The lines may intersect at a single point, and then there would be exactly one solution. Or the lines will be the same, in which case the system has infinitely many solutions, namely every point on the line itself.

   d. When we solve a linear system by method of substitution, we first solve for either variable strictly in terms of the other, say y in terms of x. We then substitute this determined value of y into the second equation and solve for the unknown variable, x in this case. Finally, we substitute this value of x into either equation and solve for y. This will give us the solution to the system provided the solution exists and that it is unique. If there is no solution, then substitution will yield a statement that can't possibly be true, for example, $0 = 3$. If there are infinitely many solutions, then substitution will never determine both variables and will lead to a statement that is always true, for example, $0 = 0$.

   e. We solve a linear system using combinations when we make the clever observation that adding or subtracting the two equations or equivalent equations could provide a cancelation of a term. This determines one of the variables, and when substituted back into either equation, determines the value of the second variable as well.

   f. To check a solution for a system, substitute the coordinates of the solution into each equation. If the solution satisfies both equations, then it is a solution to the system.

9. a. Students may draw a picture of a line with the area below the inequality shaded. The solution of an inequality of this form will be the half plane cut by the line formed by changing the inequality into an equation. Since this is a strict inequality, the line will not be part of the solution.

b. Students may draw a picture of two lines with the area below each line shaded with one section between the lines ending up shaded twice. The solution is the area that is shaded twice. A solution of a system of this form will be the quarter plane cut by two such lines and intersecting the regions of the single inequality solutions.

Looking Back and Looking Ahead

In this unit, you extended your ability to use algebraic equations and inequalities to describe and reason about geometric shapes. You also learned how to use geometric patterns to reason about systems of linear equations and inequalities.

Go Online
PHSchool.com
For: Vocabulary Review Puzzle
Web Code: apj-7051

Use Your Understanding:
Connecting Geometry and Algebra

Demonstrate your understanding of the relationships between algebra and coordinate geometry by solving the following problems.

1. The equations for the two circles below are $(x + 3)^2 + y^2 = 25$ and $(x - 3)^2 + y^2 = 25$.

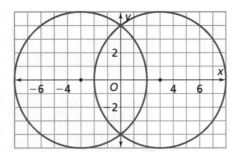

a. Tell which equation represents each circle. Explain.

b. Estimate the coordinates of the intersection points. Check by substituting the coordinates into the equations.

c. Show that $(-7, 3)$ is on the left circle in two ways:
- Show that the coordinates satisfy the given equation.
- Show geometrically that the point is 5 units from the center.

d. Show that $(-1, -3)$ is on the right circle in the two ways described in part (c).

e. Write an inequality describing the interior of each circle. Find two points in the interior of each circle and check that they satisfy the appropriate inequality.

Looking Back and Looking Ahead   **83**

Notes _____

_____

_____

_____

2. The figure below is a rectangle.

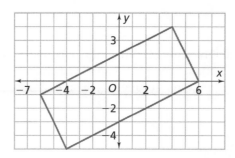

a. Use slopes to show that opposite sides are parallel.

b. Use slopes to show that adjacent sides are perpendicular.

c. Find the coordinates of the midpoints of the sides.

d. What kind of quadrilateral is formed when you connect the midpoints in order? Explain.

3. To encourage attendance to Talent Night, a school offers discounted tickets to students wearing school colors. Full-price tickets cost $9 and discounted tickets cost only $6. In all, 250 tickets are sold for a total of $2,100.

a. Let *x* represent the number of full-price tickets sold. Let *y* represent the number of discounted tickets sold. Write a system of equations to represent the information about the ticket sales.

b. Solve the system of equations in three ways.

- Use a graph to estimate.
- Use substitution.
- Use the combination method.

Notes

4. The Pep Club sells popcorn and juice at basketball games. The club earns $1.20 for each bag of popcorn and $0.80 for each cup of juice.

   a. The club's goal is to earn at least $50 at each game. Let x represent the number of bags of popcorn sold, and let y represent the number of cups of juice sold. Write an inequality to represent the club's goal.

   b. Find at least five (x, y) pairs that satisfy the inequality in part (a). Sketch a graph that represents all the solutions.

   c. The club must buy supplies. They spend $0.15 for each bag and $0.20 for each cup. Suppose the club can spend at most $15 on supplies for each game. Write an inequality for this constraint.

   d. Find at least five (x, y) pairs that satisfy the inequality in part (c). Sketch a graph of the inequality on the same axes you used in part (b). Label the region that shows the (x, y) pairs that satisfy both constraints.

Explain Your Reasoning

In this unit, you began by using algebraic equations and inequalities to describe key points on geometric figures.

5. Describe how you can write an equation or inequality that describes the coordinates of the points on each figure.

   a. a circle of radius r centered at the origin $(0, 0)$

   b. the interior of a circle of radius r centered at the origin $(0, 0)$

6. Describe how you can use the coordinates of the vertices of a quadrilateral to verify each of the following.

   a. opposite sides are parallel

   b. adjacent sides are perpendicular

7. Describe how to use coordinates of the endpoints of a segment to find the coordinates of the midpoint.

Looking Back and Looking Ahead   **85**

Notes _____

_____

_____

_____

You also used graphs and algebraic reasoning to solve systems of linear equations and inequalities.

8. Consider systems of linear equations in the form $\begin{cases} ax + by = c \\ dx + ey = f. \end{cases}$

   a. What graph shape do you expect when the solutions of each equation are plotted separately?

   b. How will the solution to the system be shown when the two equations are graphed on the same axis?

   c. What numbers of solutions are possible for a system in this form? How are these possibilities shown by the graphs?

   d. How can you solve such a system by using substitution?

   e. How can you solve such a system by using the combination method?

   f. How can you check the solution of a system?

9. a. What will a graph of a linear inequality in the form $ax + by < c$ look like?

   b. What might a graph of a system of *two* linear inequalities of the form $ax + by < c$ look like?

Look Ahead

In future mathematical studies, you will extend your understanding and skill in working with algebraic equations that represent geometric shapes and their properties. You will also learn more ways to use graphs and drawings to illustrate conditions and solutions in algebraic problems.

Notes _____

_____

_____

_____

C

chord A line segment with endpoints on a circle. Segments *CD* and *AB* in the diagram below are chords.

cuerda Segmento de recta cuyos extremos están sobre un círculo. Los segmentos *CD* y *AB* en el diagrama de abajo son cuerdas.

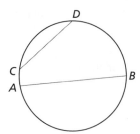

circle A geometric figure consisting of all points *P* that are a fixed distance *r* from a point *C,* called the center of the circle.

círculo Figura geométrica que consiste en que todos los puntos de *P* están a una distancia fija *r* del punto *C,* llamado centro del círculo.

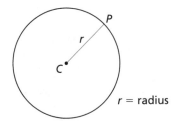

r = radius

L

linear equation in standard form The form $ax + by = c$ of a linear equation. Each side of the equation is a linear expression. The equation $6x + 3y = 12$ is in standard form. Although the slope-intercept form, $y = mx + b$, is common and useful, it is not generally considered the "standard form."

Ecuación lineal en forma general La forma $ax + by = c$ de una ecuación lineal. La ecuación $6x + 3y = 12$ está en forma general. Aunque la forma pendiente-intercepto, $y = mx + b$, es común y útil, por lo general no se considera "la forma general".

linear inequality A mathematical sentence, such as $ax + by + c < dx + ey + f$, which expresses a relationship of inequality between two quantities, each of which is a linear expression. For example, $y < -2x + 4$, and $6x + 3y \geq 12$ are linear inequalities, as are $x < 3$ and $2x + 3 < 7x$.

desigualdad lineal Enunciado matemático, como $3x + 22 < 8x + 7$ ó $3x + 4y \geq 12$ que expresa la relación de desigualdad entre dos cantidades, con cada cantidad como función lineal de una o más variables.

STUDENT PAGE

Notes _____

_____

_____

_____

midpoint A point on a line segment that is equidistant from the endpoints of the segment. Point M is the midpoint of $\overline{AB}$.

punto medio Punto en un segmento de recta que es equidistante de los extremos del segmento. El punto M es el punto medio de $\overline{AB}$.

S

system of linear equations Two or more linear equations that represent constraints on the variables used. A solution of a system of equations is a pair of values that satisfies all the equations in the system. For example, the ordered pair $(1, 2)$ is the solution of the system because it satisfies both equations.

$$\begin{cases} 6x + 3y = 12 \\ -2x + y = 0 \end{cases}$$

sistema de ecuaciones lineales Combinación de dos o más ecuaciones lineales. Una solución de un sistema de ecuaciones es un par de valores que satisface todas las ecuaciones del sistema. Por ejemplo, el par ordenado $(1, 2)$ es la solución del sistema porque satisface ambas ecuaciones.

$$\begin{cases} 6x + 3y = 12 \\ -2x + y = 0 \end{cases}$$

system of linear inequalities Two or more linear inequalities that represent constraints on the variables used. A solution of a system of inequalities is a pair of values that satisfies all the inequalities in the system. The solution of the system

$$\begin{cases} 6x + 3y < 12 \\ -2x + y > 0 \end{cases}$$

is indicated by region A in the graph below. All the points in this region satisfy *both* inequalities. The points in region B satisfy $6x + 3y < 12$, but *not* $-2x + y > 0$. The points in region C satisfy $-2x + y > 0$, but *not* $6x + 3y < 12$. The points in the unshaded region do not satisfy either inequality.

sistema de desigualdades lineales Combinación de dos o más desigualdades. Una solución de un sistema de desigualdades es un par de valores que satisface todas las desigualdades en el sistema. La solución del sistema

$$\begin{cases} 6x + 3y < 12 \\ -2x + y > 0 \end{cases}$$

está indicada por la región A en la gráfica de abajo. Todos los puntos en esta región satisfacen *ambas* desigualdades. Los puntos en la región B satisfacen $6x + 3y < 12$, pero *no* $-2x + y > 0$. Los puntos en la región C satisfacen $-2x + y > 0$, pero *no* $6x + 3y < 12$. Los puntos en la región sin sombrear no satisfacen ninguna desigualdad.

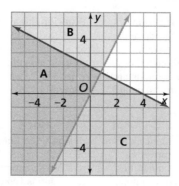

88 The Shapes of Algebra

Notes _____

_____

_____

_____

Academic Vocabulary

The following terms are important to your understanding of the mathematics in this unit. Knowing and using these words will help you in thinking, reasoning, representing, communicating your ideas, and making connections across ideas. When these words make sense to you, the investigations and problems will make more sense as well.

C

compare To tell or show how two things are alike and different.
related terms: analyze, relate

Sample: Compare the slopes of the lines $-6x + y = 12$ and $2y = 12x + 3$.

> I can write the equations of both lines in slope-intercept form to find their slopes.
> $-6x + y = 12$ $\qquad$ $2y = 12x + 3$
> $\qquad y = 6x + 12$ $\qquad$ $y = 6x + \frac{3}{2}$
> The slopes are equal. The lines are parallel since they have the same slope but a different *y*-intercept.

comparar Decir o mostrar en qué se parecen y en qué son diferentes dos cosas.
términos relacionados: analizar, relacionar

Ejemplo: Compara las pendientes de las rectas $-6x + y = 12$ y $2y = 12x + 3$.

> Puedo escribir las ecuaciones de ambas rectas en la forma pendiente, intercepto, y ordenada para hallar sus pendientes.
> $-6x + y = 12$ $\qquad$ $2y = 12x + 3$
> $\qquad y = 6x + 12$ $\qquad$ $y = 6x + \frac{3}{2}$
> Las pendientes son iguales. Las rectas son paralelas puesto que tienen la misma pendiente pero un intercepto y diferente.

D

decide To use the given information and related facts to find a value or make a decision.
related terms: determine, find, conclude

Sample: Decide whether to use equivalent form, substitution, or combination method to solve the system $\begin{cases} x - y = 8 \\ 3x + y = 4 \end{cases}$. Then solve the system.

> The coefficients of *y* in the two equations are opposites, so the combination method is a good method.
> $(x - y) + (3x + y) = 8 + 4$
> $\qquad\qquad 4x = 12$
> $\qquad\qquad\ x = 3$
> $\qquad\ x - y = 8$
> $\qquad\ 3 - y = 8$
> $\qquad\quad -y = 5$
> $\qquad\qquad y = -5$
> The solution to the system is $(3, -5)$.

decidir Usar la información dada y datos relacionados para hallar un valor o tomar una decisión.
términos relacionados: determinar, hallar, concluir

Ejemplo: Decide si debes usar un método escribiendo en forma equivalente, por sustitución o por combinación para resolver el sistema $\begin{cases} x - y = 8 \\ 3x + y = 4 \end{cases}$. Luego resuelve el sistema.

> Los coeficientes de *y* en las dos ecuaciones son opuestos, así que el método por combinación es un buen método.
> $(x - y) + (3x + y) = 8 + 4$
> $\qquad\qquad 4x = 12$
> $\qquad\qquad\ x = 3$
> $\qquad\ x - y = 8$
> $\qquad\ 3 - y = 8$
> $\qquad\quad -y = 5$
> $\qquad\qquad y = -5$
> La solución al sistema es $(3, -5)$.

Academic Vocabulary $\quad$ **89**

Notes

explain To give facts and details that make an idea easier to understand. Explaining can involve a written summary supported by a diagram, chart, table, or a combination of these.

related terms: analyze, clarify, describe, justify, tell

Sample: **What is the length of *a*? Explain your reasoning.**

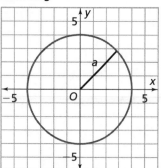

Segment *a* is a radius of the circle because it connects the center of the circle to a point on the circle. The center of the circle is at the origin and the point (4, 0) lies on the circle. So the length of the radius is 4 units. Since the lengths of all radii of a given circle are equal, *a* is also 4 units in length.

explicar Dar hechos y detalles que hacen que una idea sea más fácil de comprender. Explicar puede implicar un resumen escrito apoyado por un diagrama, una gráfica, una tabla o una combinación de éstos.

términos relacionados: analizar, aclarar, describir, justificar, decir

Ejemplo: **¿Cuál es la longitud de *a*? Explica tu razonamiento.**

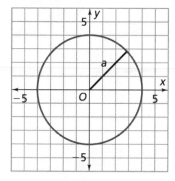

El segmento *a* es un radio del círculo porque conecta el centro del círculo con un punto en el círculo. El centro del círculo está en el origen y el punto (4, 0) se encuentra en el círculo. Así que la longitud del radio es de 4 unidades. Puesto que las longitudes de todos los radios de un círculo dado son iguales, *a* también tiene 4 unidades de longitud.

identify To match a definition or a description to an object or to recognize something and be able to name it.

related terms: name, find, classify

Sample: **Identify the *y*-intercept of the line $4x - 2y = 10$.**

I can find the *y*-intercept of the line by setting $x = 0$ and solving for *y*.

$$4x - 2y = 10$$
$$4(0) - 2y = 10$$
$$-2y = 10$$
$$y = -5$$

The *y*-intercept of the line is −5.

identificar Relacionar una definición o una descripción con un objeto, o bien, reconocer algo y ser capaz de nombrarlo.

términos relacionados: nombrar, hallar, clasificar

Ejemplo: **Identifica el intercepto *y* de la recta $4x - 2y = 10$.**

Puedo hallar el intercepto *y* de la recta estableciendo $x = 0$ y resolviendo para *y*.

$$4x - 2y = 10$$
$$4(0) - 2y = 10$$
$$-2y = 10$$
$$y = -5$$

El intercepto *y* de la recta es −5.

90   Shapes of Algebra

Notes _____

_____

_____

_____

Index

Index **91**

Notes _____

_____

_____

_____

92 The Shapes of Algebra

Notes _____

_____

_____

_____

Acknowledgments

Team Credits

The people who made up the **Connected Mathematics 2** team—representing editorial, editorial services, design services, and production services—are listed below. Bold type denotes core team members.

Leora Adler, Judith Buice, Kerry Cashman, Patrick Culleton, Sheila DeFazio, Richard Heater, **Barbara Hollingdale, Jayne Holman,** Karen Holtzman, **Etta Jacobs,** Christine Lee, Carolyn Lock, Catherine Maglio, **Dotti Marshall,** Rich McMahon, Eve Melnechuk, Kristin Mingrone, Terri Mitchell, **Marsha Novak,** Irene Rubin, Donna Russo, Robin Samper, Siri Schwartzman, **Nancy Smith,** Emily Soltanoff, **Mark Tricca,** Paula Vergith, Roberta Warshaw, Helen Young

Additional Credits

Diana Bonfilio, Mairead Reddin, Michael Torocsik, nSight, Inc.

Technical Illustration

WestWords, Inc.

Cover Design

tom white.images

Photos

2, Richard Haynes; **3,** Janet Foster/Masterfile; **5,** Topham/The Image Works; **7,** Richard Haynes; **11,** Richard Haynes; **16,** Richard Haynes; **24,** Spencer Ainsley/The Image Works; **27,** Richard Haynes; **33,** Arthur Tilley/Getty Images, Inc.; **37,** Richard Haynes; **40,** Jeff Greenberg/PhotoEdit; **42,** Siri Schwartzman; **49,** Yellow Dog Productions/Getty Images, Inc.; **52,** Bill Barley/SuperStock; **55,** Richard Haynes; **59,** Patrick Ben Luke Syder/Lonely Planet Images; **62,** David Grossman/The Image Works; **65,** Kwame Zikomo/SuperStock; **69,** Steve Craft/Masterfile; **73,** Peter Hvizdak/The Image Works; **76,** Chuck Savage/Corbis; **79,** Park Street/PhotoEdit; **84,** Dennis MacDonald/PhotoEdit

Note: Every effort has been made to locate the copyright owner of the material reprinted in this book. Omissions brought to our attention will be corrected in subsequent editions.

Notes

_____

_____

_____

_____

Labsheet 1.2

....

Crop Circle Design and Incomplete Figures

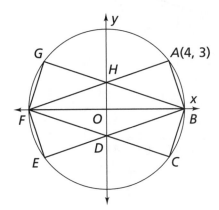

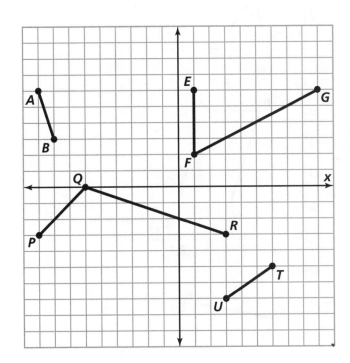

Labsheet 1ACE Exercises 3 and 4

3.

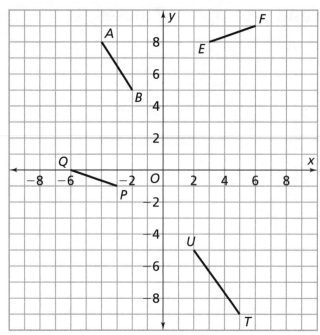

4.

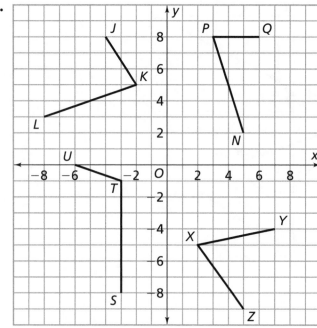

Labsheet 3.1

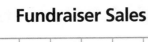

Fundraiser Sales

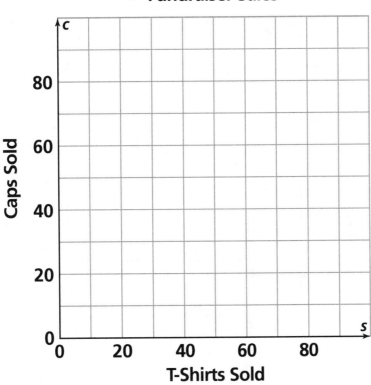

Labsheet 3.3

Student/Adult Membership Graph

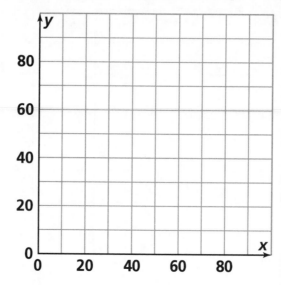

Labsheet 5.1

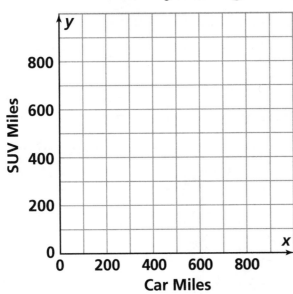

Monthly Mileage

PACING: _____

Mathematical Goals

_____

_____

_____

_____

Launch

_____
_____
_____
_____
_____
_____
_____

Materials

Explore

_____
_____
_____
_____
_____
_____
_____

Materials

Summarize

_____
_____
_____
_____
_____
_____
_____

Materials

C

chord A line segment with endpoints on a circle. Segments *CD* and *AB* in the diagram below are chords.

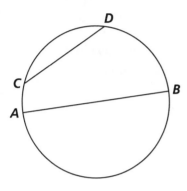

circle A geometric figure consisting of all points *P* that are a fixed distance *r* from a point *C*, called the center of the circle.

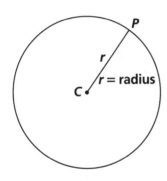

L

linear equation in standard form The form $ax + by = c$ of a linear equation. Each side of the equation is a linear expression. The equation $6x + 3y = 12$ is in standard form. Although the slope-intercept form, $y = mx + b$, is common and useful, it is not generally considered the "standard form."

M

midpoint A point on a line segment that is equidistant from the endpoints of the segment. Point *M* is the midpoint of $\overline{AB}$.

S

system of linear equations Two or more linear equations which represent constraints on the variables used. A solution of a system of equations is a pair of values that satisfies all the equations in the system. For example, the ordered pair $(1, 2)$ is the solution of the system because it satisfies both equations.

$$\begin{cases} 6x + 3y = 12 \\ -2x + y = 0 \end{cases}$$

system of linear inequalities Two or more linear inequalities which represent constraints on the variables used. A solution of a system of inequalities is a pair of values that satisfies all the inequalities in the system. The solution of the system

$$\begin{cases} 3x + 6y < 12 \\ -2x + y > 0 \end{cases}$$

is indicated by region A in the graph below. All the points in this region satisfy *both* inequalities. The points in region C satisfy $3x + 6y < 12$, but *not* $-2x + y > 0$. The points in region B satisfy $-2x + y > 0$, but not $3x + 6y < 12$. The points in the unshaded region do not satisfy either inequality.

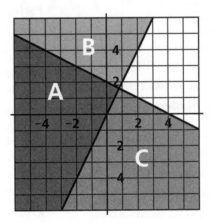

Index

Acknowledgments

Team Credits

The people who made up the **Connected Mathematics 2** team—representing editorial, editorial services, design services, and production services—are listed below. Bold type denotes core team members.

Leora Adler, Judith Buice, Kerry Cashman, Patrick Culleton, Sheila DeFazio, Richard Heater, **Barbara Hollingdale, Jayne Holman,** Karen Holtzman, **Etta Jacobs,** Christine Lee, Carolyn Lock, Catherine Maglio, **Dotti Marshall,** Rich McMahon, Eve Melnechuk, Kristin Mingrone, Terri Mitchell, **Marsha Novak,** Irene Rubin, Donna Russo, Robin Samper, Siri Schwartzman, **Nancy Smith,** Emily Soltanoff, **Mark Tricca,** Paula Vergith, Roberta Warshaw, Helen Young

Additional Credits

Diana Bonfilio, Mairead Reddin, Michael Torocsik, nSight, Inc.

Technical Illustration

Schawk, Inc.

Cover Design

tom white.images